# MathLand™

## Journeys Through Mathematics

Charles • Randolph Brummett • McDonald • Westley

# ASSESSMENT GUIDE

GRADE
4

**Creative Publications**®
**Mountain View, CA**

Contributing Writers • Nancy Rogers Bosse, Alison Wells, Janet Pittock,
Ann Roper, Kim Thoman, Bee Thorpe
Project Editors • Sandra Ward, Lynn Sanchez, Kelly Stewart, Nora Sweeny, Connie Thorpe, Rhea Irvine
Production Editors • Lynn Damme, Cheryl Turner
Editorial Consultant • Frank Tarsitano

Classroom Coordinators • Heather McDonald, Kathryn Walker, Cynthia Reak,
Julie Brodie, Maile Sweeney, Sarah Pressler

Creative Director • Ken Shue
Art Director • JoAnne Hammer
Senior Designer • Elaine Abe Strocher
Contributing Designers • Violeta Diaz, Sharon Spurlock
Senior Illustrator • Pauline Phung
Electronic Publishing Coordinator • Grace Sun
Electronic Art Coordinator • Meg Babcock
Illustrators • Violeta Diaz, Lilia Kim, Jane Likens, Mark Pule, Joan Takenaka

Production Coordinators • Lisa Chang, Ed Lazar, Pat Seto, Joan Lindsay
Production Services • The Mazer Corporation, York Graphic Services

Manufacturing Director • Vickie Self
Manufacturing Coordinator • Michelle Berardinelli

Creative Publications, MathLand, LinkerCubes, ClockWorks,
Fraction Factory, Fraction Squares PLUS, Fraction Circles PLUS, and Decimal Factory
are all trademarks or registered trademarks of Creative Publications.

Second Edition
© 1998 Creative Publications
1300 Villa Street
Mountain View, CA 94041

First Edition © 1995 Creative Publications
Printed in the United States of America
ISBN: 0-7622-0294-7
1 2 3 4 5 6 7 8 9 10. 00 99 98

# Contents

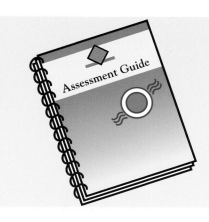

## Unit 1 • ALL ABOUT US
### Gathering, Communicating, and Interpreting Data

## Unit 2 • LOOKING FOR RULES
### Investigating the Dependable Nature of Patterns

## Unit 3 • STRATEGIES
### Building a Network of Number Relationships

## Unit 4 • THAT'S UNIQUE
### Examining Differences and Possibilities

## Unit 5 • NUMBERS BETWEEN NUMBERS
### Developing the Idea of Equivalence with Fractional Numbers

# Contents

# What Is the Philosophy of Assessment in MathLand?

The goal of MathLand is to empower students mathematically. One of the aims of assessment, therefore, is to put you in closer touch with what your students are thinking so that you may monitor and facilitate students' progress toward the achievement of mathematical power. You may select from the menu of authentic assessments on this page and the quizzes on page T3 to obtain a balanced, rich and valid picture of each student's learning.

The authentic assessments in MathLand are an integral part of the instructional program and are designed to provide you with ongoing information about what your students know and can do. The assessments are described below and discussed on subsequent pages.

| Type of Assessment | Purpose | When to Use |
|---|---|---|
| Observation | Observations provide insights not only into students' thinking, but also into their interpersonal skills and learning dispositions, information not available from the students' work products alone. | Continuously |
| Written | This question can help you determine individual student's understandings of one of the unit's big ideas. It is also an opportunity for students to gain more experience in writing about their thinking. | Before or after unit or both |
| Interview | This is a question to ask as students are engaged in an activity, or to use in a separate interview of any students about whose thinking you need to know more. | During unit (Along the Way) or independent work times |
| Self-Assessment | This question prompts students to reflect on what they have learned, the process of learning, or their disposition toward mathematics. | Portfolio Review Math Journal Anytime |
| Portfolio Review | Reviewing portfolios adds detail to your overall impression of a student's mathematical understandings. Students' review of their work gives them a chance to revise, reflect and take responsibility for learning. Families are informed by work portfolios sent home and assessment portfolios shared at conferences. | End of week and/or End of unit |

## Guiding Principles for an Assessment Program

Assessment should:

- Provide a variety of ways for students to reveal what they know and demonstrate what they can do in mathematics.

- Support students' learning and help teachers make instructional decisions.

- Hold high standards for all students and give teachers and students tools to meet those standards.

- Provide a balanced, rich and complex body of information about each student.

## What Is Assessed in MathLand?

The assessments in the MathLand units reflect a holistic philosophy that looks at the complete development of the student. In addition to looking for understanding of the Key Mathematical Ideas, teachers are encouraged to observe students' abilities to communicate their ideas as well as their dispositions toward learning. The different types of assessments offered help teachers collect this information.

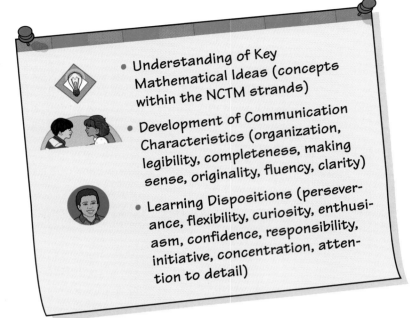

- Understanding of Key Mathematical Ideas (concepts within the NCTM strands)
- Development of Communication Characteristics (organization, legibility, completeness, making sense, originality, fluency, clarity)
- Learning Dispositions (perseverance, flexibility, curiosity, enthusiasm, confidence, responsibility, initiative, concentration, attention to detail)

## The Scoring Rubric

The Assessment Guide suggests a general three-point rubric to use as a guide. Students' work can be sorted into three piles that you identify as Level 3, Level 2, and Level 1 responses based on the rubric.

You may wish to sort work into four or five categories. A Level 4 added to the three-point rubric can identify responses that go beyond the requirements of the task—showing unique solutions, extending the task, or making connections.

One way to create a five-point rubric is to modify the four-point rubric. Keep Levels 1 and 3 and use the Level 4 description for Level 5. Levels 2 and 4 describe responses that fall between Levels 1, 3, and 5. They do not need to be described in the rubric, but may be defined as partial and substantial accomplishments.

Student-generated rubrics are a powerful tool for helping students take responsibility for their learning and produce work that meets high standards. You may refer to pages Q83–Q87 in the Resource Manager for additional resources on the use of rubrics.

Sharing rubrics with parents and building a collection of exemplary student work are other ways you can help everyone understand the criteria by which work is assessed and the standard of work expected.

### Response Levels

**3** Accomplishes the purposes of the question, task, or unit. Mathematical communication is clear.

**2** Partially accomplishes the purposes of the question, task, or unit. Mathematical communication is somewhat limited.

**1** Shows fragmented understanding. Mathematical communication is vague.

## How Are Skills Assessed in MathLand?

There are many opportunities to assess the development of students' skills in MathLand. The unit activities let you assess how well students put skills to work in significant pieces of mathematical work. In addition, several ways to check up on individual students' skills using the Skill Power student component and the MathLand quizzes are available.

## In the MathLand Units:

The Portfolio Review pages in the Assessment Guide include descriptions of the levels at which students may put skills to work in the unit activities. Selecting student work and observation notes for portfolios will let you assess how students apply skills over time.

## In Skill Power:

The Skill Power book is designed to provide teachers with more than just students' answers. Students' explanations of their solutions provide information about and create a record of their developing number sense and computation strategies. Assessment Tips for teachers appear throughout the teachers' edition of Skill Power.

## In the MathLand Quizzes — three ways to get a quick picture:

Three types of optional reproducible quizzes appear in the Assessment section of the Resource Manager, pages Q1–Q64. You may decide to use these short written assessments with the whole class, or with small groups or individuals about whom you want additional information.

| | Type of Quiz | Purpose | When to Use |
|---|---|---|---|
| 20 | Daily Tune-Up Reviews* | These quick review exercises cover the Daily Tune-Ups skills practiced over the preceding nineteen days. | Every 4 weeks |
| 1 | Computation Checks | This mixed set of twenty problems will let you see how well students are maintaining old computation skills and employing new ones. | Quarterly |
| UNIT Review | Unit Reviews | Enhanced multiple-choice and short constructed-response questions ask students to use key understandings. | After the unit |

*Another version of the Daily Tune-Up Reviews — one designed to be presented orally by the teacher — appears in your Daily Tune-Ups book every 20 pages.

## Using the Assessment Overview

At the beginning of the assessment section for each unit, you will see an Assessment Overview. **Before the Unit** tells you in advance what the Key Mathematical Ideas for the unit are, and suggests Communication Characteristics and Learning Dispositions that are particularly important for the unit. You will want to keep these aspects in mind as you observe students and review their work during the course of the unit.

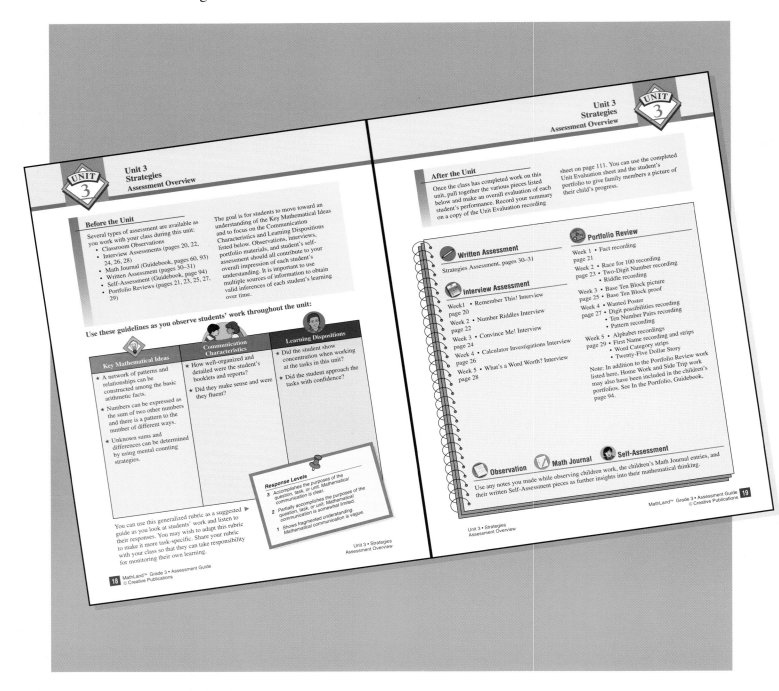

**After the Unit** relates to the Unit Summary page in the Guidebook. For your convenience, this page lists all the different pieces of work it will be possible to have for each student at the unit's completion. Unit Summary is a time to think about each student's performance as a whole during the unit.

If you wish to give each student an overall rating for the unit, use the 3-2-1 rubric or a rubric or system of your choice. Record this and your overall impressions on the Unit Evaluation sheet, page 111.

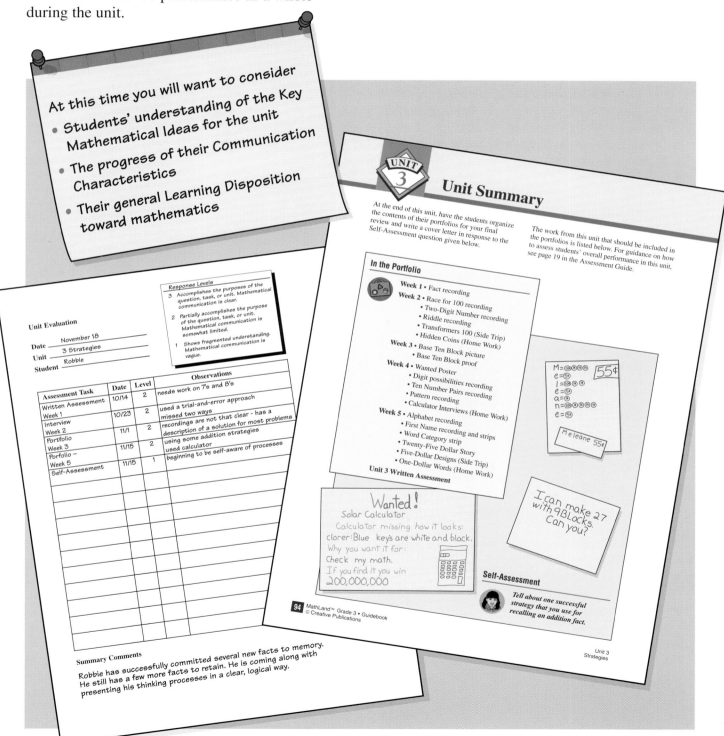

## The Importance of Observations

In MathLand there are daily opportunities to observe students working in small groups and in class discussions. When your observations are recorded and organized they become a valid and important part of the assessment profile for each student, and they can be shared with others.

Many teachers find they need to experiment with various recording methods and learn to make brief recordings in order to create the system of note taking that works best for them.

**Clipboards** work well when you want to use a checklist to make observations about specific aspects of students' learning. Clipboards can also hold forms for making anecdotal records of your observations of selected students. See page T7 for information about the recording forms provided in MathLand.

**Notes on file cards** are easy to carry around and can be filed alphabetically with name, date, and an observation or two.

**Sticky Labels** kept in your pocket are handy for spontaneous notes which you can place in your records later.

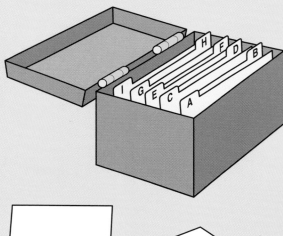

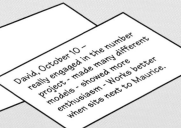

David, October 10 – really engaged in the number project - made many different models - showed more enthusiasm - Works better when site next to Maurice.

**Class Grid Sheets** are another way to record daily observations for the whole class. Each box on the grid has one student's name and any notes or observations you make.

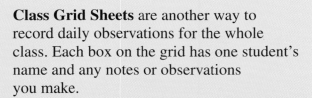

## Where to Record

A variety of recording options are provided in this guide and the Resource Manager. You may use the task-specific Performance Observations sheet on page 110 of this guide to record comments about several students as they work, or to capture students' understandings of the Written Assessment and Interview Assessment tasks. The Unit Evaluation sheet on page 111 lets you summarize all of your observations of an individual student.

The Resource Manager provides a collection of forms for managing assessments. Pages Q66–Q82 provide forms for parents, teachers, and students to use in creating and responding to portfolios. Suggestions and templates for using rubrics appear on pages Q83–Q87. Forms for recording observations and interviews as well as computation and problem-solving skills checklists are provided on pages Q88–Q94.

## Using the Interview Assessment

MathLand provides one Interview Assessment question for each week. This question appears in the Guidebook with a reference to the appropriate pages in the Assessment Guide.

 Some Interview Assessment questions are designed to be used while the students are engaged in work on the unit activity. As you circulate around the room observing students, you may stop and pose this question to one student at a time informally.

Other Interview Assessments present questions or tasks separate from the work students are engaged in. These take time, but can help you gain insights into the thinking of students about whom you need additional information.

Use the Performance Observations recording sheet on page 110 or the Interview Record on page Q94 of the Resource Manager to keep track of whom you have interviewed and to record your comments.

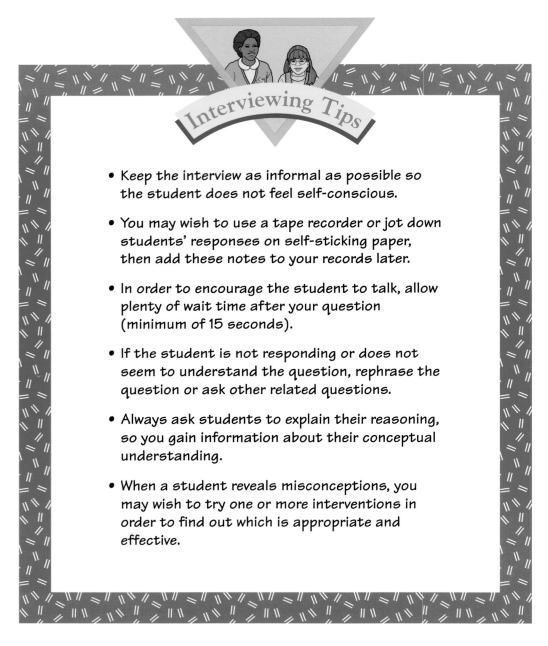

### Interviewing Tips

- Keep the interview as informal as possible so the student does not feel self-conscious.

- You may wish to use a tape recorder or jot down students' responses on self-sticking paper, then add these notes to your records later.

- In order to encourage the student to talk, allow plenty of wait time after your question (minimum of 15 seconds).

- If the student is not responding or does not seem to understand the question, rephrase the question or ask other related questions.

- Always ask students to explain their reasoning, so you gain information about their conceptual understanding.

- When a student reveals misconceptions, you may wish to try one or more interventions in order to find out which is appropriate and effective.

Overall, the assessment program in MathLand provides a variety of ways for students to reveal what they know about mathematics. This is particularly important with second-language learners. When interviewing students learning English, it may be useful to have another student help the second-language learner understand your questions. It is important to keep in mind that students may understand more than they can express verbally.

The Interview Assessment page in the Assessment Guide provides:

- The question you will be asking
- Samples of possible responses
- Descriptions of those responses and how they might be leveled

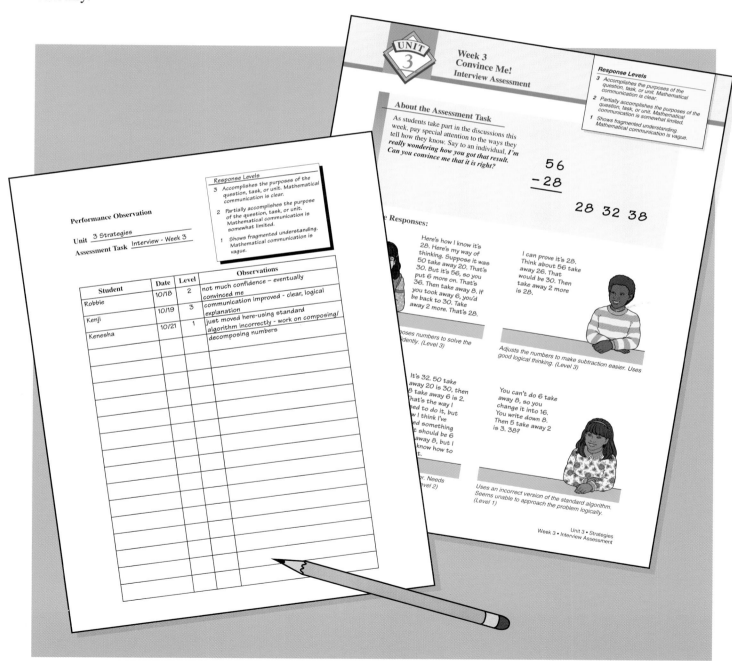

## Using the Written Assessment

One formal Written Assessment task per unit is offered in the Assessment Guide. Use it at any time during the unit to gain information about students' thinking in regard to one aspect of the unit's subject matter. It is not intended as an evaluation of the entire scope of the unit. You may choose to use it with the whole class or with only those students for whom you need additional information.

The Written Assessment page provides:

- The question or task you will read to students
- Samples of possible individual responses
- Descriptions of those responses and how they might be leveled

Use copies of the Performance Observations recording sheet on page 110 to keep track of your levels and observations.

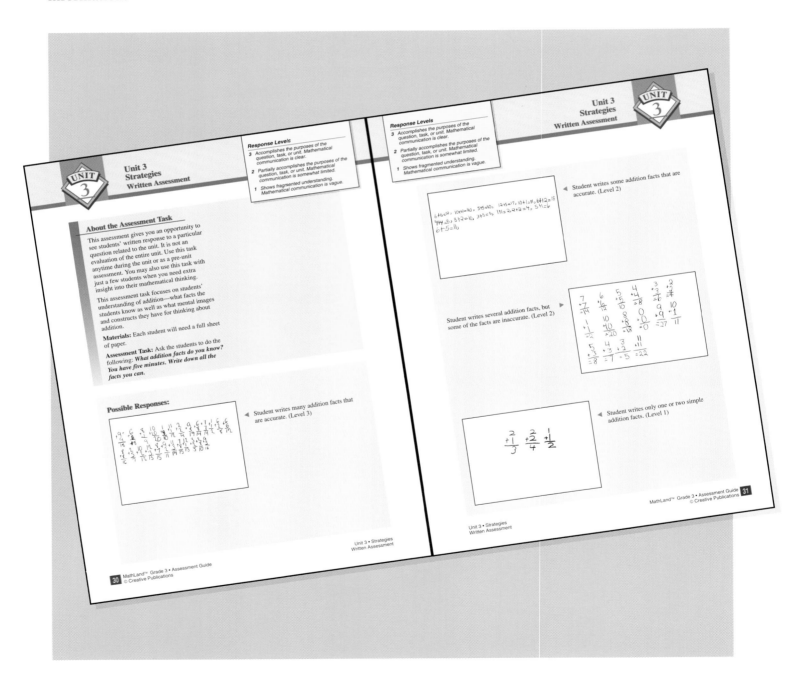

## Using Self-Assessment

MathLand provides Self-Assessment questions on a regular basis. These questions can be found on the Unit Summary page in the Guidebook.

 The self-assessment questions prompt students to reflect on their learning. Using rubrics to guide and revise their work, building assessment portfolios, and writing in response to the self-assessment questions all help students grow in self-awareness and the ability to be responsible for their own learning.

## Math Journals

 Math Journal entries can provide added insights into a student's thinking, understanding, and disposition.

Journals kept throughout the school year are a wonderful vehicle for extended, individual conversations with students. You may respond to students' entries with brief notes—showing appreciation of thinking, acknowledging feelings, sharing ideas, responding to questions, or prompting students to clarify or extend their thinking. Provided frequently throughout the Guidebook, the optional Math Journal questions are opportunities for students to develop their writing skills as well.

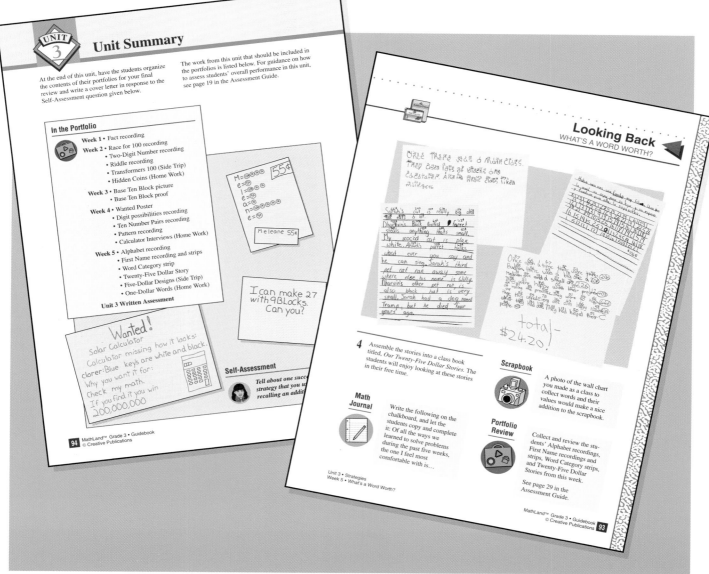

## Using the Portfolio Review

A portfolio kept over the course of a year can represent a significant body of work done by a student. The pieces of work selected for assessment portfolios can provide evidence of mathematical growth and document what the student knows and can do in relation to specific criteria.

One option for managing portfolios is to have students file their daily work in work portfolios stored in an accessible place. The Resource Manager provides a Work Portfolio Table of Contents sheet for each unit (pages Q68–Q77). Attached to the front of folders, these can help students organize their work.

Each week, the Guidebook will note what should be included in the work portfolios and will refer you to the appropriate pages in the Assessment Guide. The Portfolio Review page in the Assessment Guide provides:

• Suggestions of what to look for in the students' work that week

• Samples of possible responses

• Suggestions as to how those responses might be leveled

At the end of a unit, have students select for their assessment portfolios their best work, or work that meets other criteria you have discussed with them. Students may revise work at this time, and should attach the revisions to their original pieces of work.

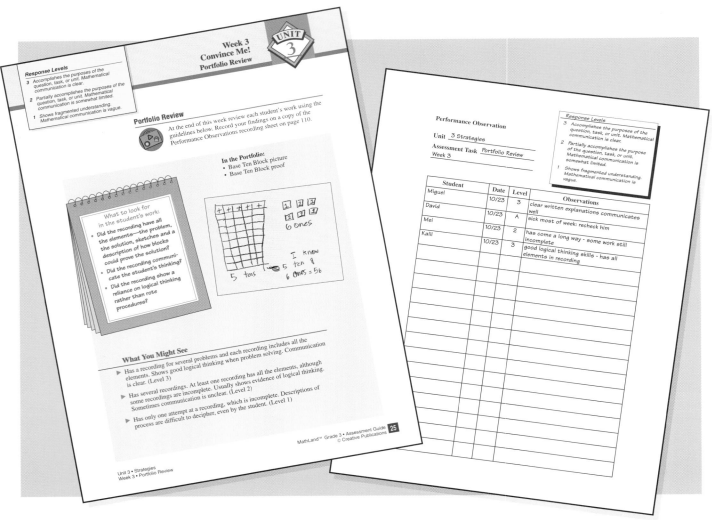

Once students pull their work together, have them write a portfolio cover letter in response to the unit's Self-Assessment question. Students may also complete a Portfolio Entry form for each piece of work.

When you have reviewed students' work and made selections for their portfolios, give students timely feedback. Send work portfolios home periodically to help families interact with their child and understand your mathematics program.

Pages Q66–Q82 of the Resource Manager provide forms to help you, parents, and students create and respond to portfolios.

**TIP** When one piece of work is generated by two students, some teachers choose to place the work in one student's portfolio and include a note in the partner's portfolio indicating which portfolio contains the collaborative work. Other teachers make photocopies of key pieces of work so they can appear in both portfolios. Another option is to have pairs work together but record and report individually.

## Communicating with Parents

The MathLand approach to both teaching and assessment is likely to be quite different from what parents experienced as children. Students working together, talking about mathematics, and writing about their thinking may all be new ideas to parents who think of mathematics as mostly arithmetic. MathLand provides you with the following materials to help you talk with parents about these new ideas.

### Introducing Parents to

- Send home the introductory Family Letter from the Resource Manager, page T8. The letter tells parents what to expect during the year and also includes a summary of the MathLand philosophy.

- Use pages T1 and T3 in this guide as you talk with parents about assessment. These pages show charts describing each type of assessment in the program. You may reproduce the charts and send them home, or use them during conferences. Pages T4–T13 in this guide, and Q1, Q9, and Q33–Q34 in the Resource Manager provide more information about each type of assessment.

- At Back To School Night, explain how rubrics will be used and describe what is assessed in MathLand: an understanding of key mathematical ideas, and the development of communication skills and learning dispositions. Refer to page T2.

### Family Letters go home every week

- Send home the Family Letters each week. These are referenced in the Guidebook and contained in the Resource Manager. The Family Letter explains the math activity for the week.

- Another function of the Family Letter is to involve parents with their child's homework so they get firsthand experience with assessing how their child is learning.

### Tips for Conference Time

- The student's portfolio will provide the major source of material for discussion during conference time. It will contain selected pieces of mathematical work completed by the student during the reporting period and serve as a jumping off point for discussion of the student's understanding of key mathematical ideas, skills acquisition, communication abilities, and learning disposition. You may wish to go through it unit by unit, or you may wish to focus on selected issues and use work from the portfolio as examples to support your observations.

- Sharing your scoring rubrics will help you explain how work is assessed.

- Include observation notes as well as quizzes and selected Skill Power problems to give parents a full picture of their child's learning.

## Skill Power

Many features in this student component are designed to help parents learn about what their children are studying at school and the new as well as familiar aspects of skills practice in MathLand. Parents will find:

- Introductions to the unit concepts

- Applications families can look into at home

- Vocabulary definitions and practice activities

- Parent Notes explaining the purposes of the different types of practice pages

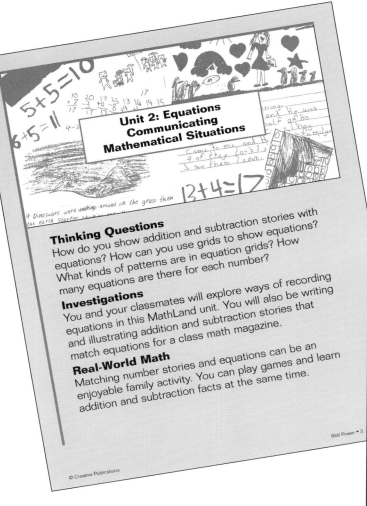

### Unit 2: Equations Communicating Mathematical Situations

**Thinking Questions**
How do you show addition and subtraction stories with equations? How can you use grids to show equations? What kinds of patterns are in equation grids? How many equations are there for each number?

**Investigations**
You and your classmates will explore ways of recording equations in this MathLand unit. You will also be writing and illustrating addition and subtraction stories that match equations for a class math magazine.

**Real-World Math**
Matching number stories and equations can be an enjoyable family activity. You can play games and learn addition and subtraction facts at the same time.

Skill Power • 2

© Creative Publications

## Bridges to Home

The MathLand parent newsletter, Bridges to Home, can be sent home at the beginning of each unit. Every issue contains:

- A description of the mathematical thinking which is the focus of the unit

- Notes about each of the investigations

- A "sprinkling" of quick math activities families can do at home

- Examples of the skills practice occurring in the Daily Tune-Ups

- Examples of math vocabulary

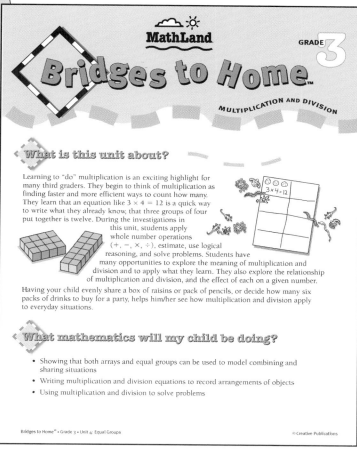

### MathLand
### Bridges to Home.
GRADE 3

MULTIPLICATION AND DIVISION

**What is this unit about?**

Learning to "do" multiplication is an exciting highlight for many third graders. They begin to think of multiplication as finding faster and more efficient ways to count how many. They learn that an equation like $3 \times 4 = 12$ is a quick way to write what they already know, that three groups of four put together is twelve. During the investigations in this unit, students apply whole number operations $(+, -, \times, \div)$, estimate, use logical reasoning, and solve problems. Students have many opportunities to explore the meaning of multiplication and division and to apply what they learn. They also explore the relationship of multiplication and division, and the effect of each on a given number.

Having your child evenly share a box of raisins or pack of pencils, or decide how many six packs of drinks to buy for a party, helps him/her see how multiplication and division apply to everyday situations.

**What mathematics will my child be doing?**

- Showing that both arrays and equal groups can be used to model combining and sharing situations
- Writing multiplication and division equations to record arrangements of objects
- Using multiplication and division to solve problems

Bridges to Home™ • Grade 3 • Unit 4: Equal Groups

© Creative Publications

# Unit 1
# All About Us
## Assessment Overview

## Before the Unit

Several types of assessment are available as you work with your class during this unit:

- Classroom Observations
- Interview Assessments (pages 4, 6)
- Math Journal (Guidebook, pages 12, 19)
- Written Assessment (pages 8–9)
- Self-Assessment (Guidebook, page 22)
- Portfolio Reviews (pages 5, 7)

The goal is for students to move toward an understanding of the Key Mathematical Ideas and to focus on the Communication Characteristics and Learning Dispositions listed below. Observations, interviews, portfolio materials, and students' self-assessments should all contribute to your overall impression of each student's understanding. It is important to use multiple sources of information to obtain valid inferences of each student's learning over time.

## Use these guidelines as you observe students' work throughout the unit:

| Key Mathematical Ideas | Communication Characteristics | Learning Dispositions |
|---|---|---|
| ★ A set of data can be organized and reported in a variety of ways. <br><br> ★ Counting, grouping, and displaying data in certain ways can help in making comparisons of data. | ★ Was the student able to organize a set of raw data and present it in a clear manner? <br><br> ★ Does the student's work show originality? <br><br> ★ Did the student's questions and answers about displays make sense to others? | ★ Did the student show responsibility in reading directions and handling other students' displays, and flexibility in following a variety of directions written by others? |

You can use this generalized rubric as a suggested guide as you look at students' work and listen to their responses. You may wish to adapt this rubric to make it more task-specific. Share your rubric with your class so that they can take responsibility for monitoring their own learning. ▶

### Response Levels

3 Accomplishes the purposes of the question, task, or unit. Mathematical communication is clear.

2 Partially accomplishes the purposes of the question, task, or unit. Mathematical communication is somewhat limited.

1 Shows fragmented understanding. Mathematical communication is vague.

## After the Unit

Once the class has completed work on this unit, pull together the various pieces listed below and make an overall evaluation of each student's performance. Record your summary on a copy of the Unit Evaluation recording sheet on page 111. You can use the completed Unit Evaluation sheet and the student's portfolio to give family members a picture of their child's progress.

 **Written Assessment**

All About Us Written Assessment, pages 8-9

 **Interview Assessment**

Week 1 • Profiles Interview
page 4

Week 2 • Preferences Interview
page 6

 **Portfolio Review**

Week 1 • Profiles displays
page 5 • Questions About Profiles displays
• Answers to questions about displays
• Statements on Venn Diagrams

Week 2 • Preferences displays with directions
page 7 • Statements based on displays

Note: In addition to the Portfolio Review work listed here, Home Work and Side Trip work may also have been included in the students' portfolios. See In the Portfolio, Guidebook, page 22.

 **Observation**   **Math Journal**   **Self-Assessment**

Use any notes you made while observing students work, the students' Math Journal entries, and their written Self-Assessment pieces as further insights into their mathematical thinking.

**Response Levels**

**3** Accomplishes the purposes of the question, task, or unit. Mathematical communication is clear.

**2** Partially accomplishes the purposes of the question, task, or unit. Mathematical communication is somewhat limited.

**1** Shows fragmented understanding. Mathematical communication is vague.

## About the Interview Assessment Task

As students work during Along the Way, show one of the students' graphs to individual students and ask, **What are some things you can tell by looking at this graph?**

## Possible Responses

I can tell that most people in our class are right-handed. Three people are left-handed.

*Is able to interpret the display, making generalizations with comparative words such as* most *and* fewest, *as well as with exact numbers. (Level 3)*

Twenty-five people are right-handed. Three are left-handed.

*Is able to interpret the display, giving exact numbers. (Level 3)*

Most people are right-handed.

*Is able to make one generalization from visual information on the display but has difficulty quantifying information. (Level 2)*

I don't know.

*Shows no ability to interpret the display, even after being given help with reading labels on graph. (Level 1)*

**Response Levels**

**3** *Accomplishes the purposes of the question, task, or unit. Mathematical communication is clear.*

**2** *Partially accomplishes the purposes of the question, task, or unit. Mathematical communication is somewhat limited.*

**1** *Shows fragmented understanding. Mathematical communication is vague.*

## Portfolio Review

 At the end of this week review each student's work using the guidelines below. Record your findings on a copy of the Performance Observations recording sheet on page 110.

What to look for
in the students' work:

- Did the student's display show the full class's results for one or more survey questions?

- Did the labels on the display indicate what information is shown and how many students had each result?

- Was the student able to write questions that a display can answer?

- Was the student able to answer questions by interpreting displays?

**In the Portfolio:**

- Questions About Profiles displays
- Answers to questions about displays
- Statements on Venn Diagrams

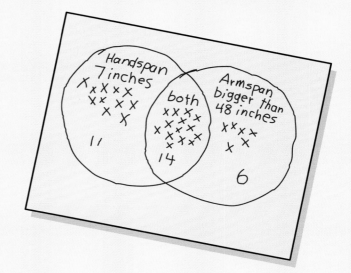

## What You Might See

▶ The display shows the full set of data and is easy to interpret without additional input from the student. Student is able to write clear questions about others' displays and answer them accurately. (Level 3)

▶ The full set of data appears to be displayed but some labels are missing. Some explanation from the student is needed to interpret the graph. Student's questions and answers about displays show some difficulty interpreting graphs. (Level 2)

▶ Some data are missing. The report and display are difficult to interpret, and student is not able to clarify them orally. Student is not able to write or answer questions about displays. (Level 1)

**Response Levels**

**3** Accomplishes the purposes of the question, task, or unit. Mathematical communication is clear.

**2** Partially accomplishes the purposes of the question, task, or unit. Mathematical communication is somewhat limited.

**1** Shows fragmented understanding. Mathematical communication is vague.

## About the Interview Assessment Task

During Along the Way, as students mark choices on surveys, say to individual students, *Tell me how you are going to mark this survey and what your mark will mean.*

## Possible Responses

I'm supposed to color in a box in line with what I like best. My mark means I prefer roller blades.

*Student restates and interprets directions correctly and explains what her mark will mean. (Level 3)*

I'm supposed to color in here. That means I like roller blades best.

*Student interprets directions correctly and explains what his mark will mean. (Level 3)*

I'm putting an X here.

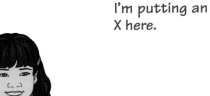
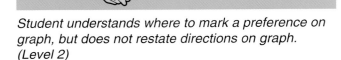

*Student understands where to mark a preference on graph, but does not restate directions on graph. (Level 2)*

I'm not sure what to do.

*Student shows limited ability to interpret instructions and display, even when instructions are read aloud. (Level 1)*

## Portfolio Review

At the end of this week review each student's work using the guidelines below. Record your findings on a copy of the Performance Observations recording sheet on page 110.

**In the Portfolio:**
- Preferences displays with directions
- Statements based on displays

### What to look for in the student's work:

- Was the student able to design a survey display?
- Were the directions for filling in the survey clear?
- Was the display organized clearly?
- Was the student able to interpret displays and write statements about the class based on them?

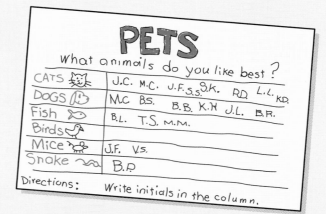

## What You Might See

▶ Student has a survey display. Directions for completing the survey are clear. Information is organized in such a way that conclusions about the whole class can be made at a glance. Student is able to write accurate statements about the class, based on the surveys. (Level 3)

▶ Student has a survey display. Directions for completing the survey are not entirely clear. The display can be interpreted with some verbal clarification from the student. Student's written statements indicate that student does not always interpret displays carefully. (Level 2)

▶ Student tries to design a survey but does not write directions. The display is difficult to interpret, even when student is asked for clarification. The student's written statements seem unrelated to the displays. (Level 1)

## Unit 1
## All About Us
### Written Assessment

## About the Written Assessment Task

This assessment gives you an opportunity to see students' written responses to a particular question related to the unit. It is not an evaluation of the entire unit. Use this task anytime during the unit or as a pre-unit assessment. You may also use this task with just a few students when you need extra insight into their mathematical thinking.

Use this task to find out something about your students' attitudes toward mathematics.

**Materials:** Each student will need paper and a pencil. You will need chart paper.

**Assessment Task:** During this unit, allow some time for students to share their ideas about mathematics. Ask them to write in response to these questions: *What are some things you already know about mathematics? What do you think you might learn about mathematics this year?*

Ask students to share their responses and write some of them on chart paper. Save the chart paper; you will use it again toward the end of the school year for the Reflections Week activities. The students will enjoy seeing their responses from the beginning of the year and reflecting on how far they have come in the year.

With the Written Assessment tasks in subsequent units you will have the opportunity to assess the Response Levels of individual student's responses. For this first Written Assessment, you may simply jot down any observations you have about students' attitudes and their abilities to communicate what they think and know about the subject of mathematics.

## Possible Responses

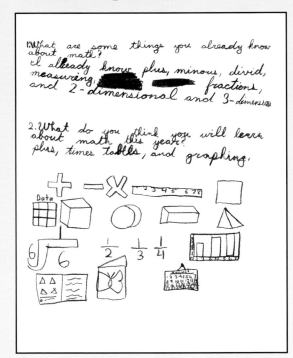

**Response Levels**

**3** Accomplishes the purposes of the question, task, or unit. Mathematical communication is clear.

**2** Partially accomplishes the purposes of the question, task, or unit. Mathematical communication is somewhat limited.

**1** Shows fragmented understanding. Mathematical communication is vague.

Unit 1
All About Us
**Written Assessment**

1. What are something you already know about math?
Adding, Substracting, fractions, inches, centermeter, mesure, money, counting, time table, Mustibacotione tales, Graphing, Machine, time telling, colcalating.
2. What do you think you will learn this year?
I think I will learn Algerbra, yards, cashing, earning money, pricing, Maping, learning other area in other Contonets.

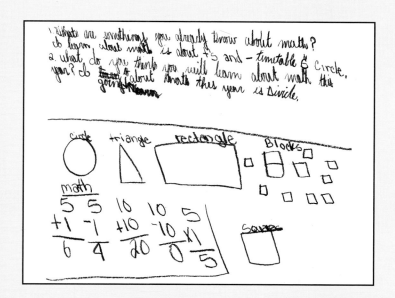

1. What are somethings you already know about math? I learn about math is about + 's and - timetable & circle.
2. what do you think you will learn about math this year? I going to learn about math this year is Divide.

circle   triangle   rectangle   Blocks

math
5   5   10   10   5
+1   -1   +10   -10   ×1
6   4   20   0   5

soupe

## Before the Unit

Several types of assessment are available as you work with your class during this unit:

- Classroom Observations
- Interview Assessments (pages 12, 14)
- Math Journal (Guidebook, pages 37, 45)
- Written Assessment (pages 16–17)
- Self-Assessment (Guidebook, page 46)
- Portfolio Reviews (pages 13, 15)

The goal is for students to move toward an understanding of the Key Mathematical Ideas and to focus on the Communication Characteristics and Learning Dispositions listed below. Observations, interviews, portfolio materials, and students' self-assessments should all contribute to your overall impression of each student's understanding. It is important to use multiple sources of information to obtain valid inferences of each student's learning over time.

## Use these guidelines as you observe students' work throughout the unit:

| Key Mathematical Ideas | Communication Characteristics | Learning Dispositions |
|---|---|---|
| ★ Patterns are governed by rules, which can be used for making predictions.<br><br>★ Patterns can be used to solve problems or make discoveries about numbers.<br><br>★ The factors of a number can be modeled with rectangles. | ★ Was the student able to describe rules governing patterns and use them to make predictions in an organized way?<br><br>★ Did the student's recordings about factors, multiples, and primes make sense? | ★ Did the student show perseverance when working on an extended project?<br><br>★ Was the student flexible when approaching problems, trying new methods if a method did not work?<br><br>★ Was the student attentive to detail? |

You can use this generalized rubric as a suggested guide as you look at students' work and listen to their responses. You may wish to adapt this rubric to make it more task-specific. Share your rubric with your class so that they can take responsibility for monitoring their own learning. ▶

**Response Levels**

3   Accomplishes the purposes of the question, task, or unit. Mathematical communication is clear.

2   Partially accomplishes the purposes of the question, task, or unit. Mathematical communication is somewhat limited.

1   Shows fragmented understanding. Mathematical communication is vague.

### After the Unit

Once the class has completed work on this unit, pull together the various pieces listed below and make an overall evaluation of each student's performance. Record your summary on a copy of the Unit Evaluation recording sheet on page 111. You can use the completed Unit Evaluation sheet and the student's portfolio to give family members a picture of their child's progress.

 **Written Assessment**

Looking for Rules Written Assessment, pages 16–17

 **Interview Assessment**

Week 1 • Red Fence, Green Gate Interview
page 12

Week 2 • Rectangle Factory Interview
page 14

 **Portfolio Review**

Week 1 • Red Fence, Green Gate recordings
page 13

Week 2 • Reports on factors, multiples or
page 15    primes

Note: In addition to the Portfolio Review work listed here, Home Work and Side Trip work may also have been included in the students' portfolios. See In the Portfolio, Guidebook, page 46.

 **Observation**    **Math Journal**    **Self-Assessment**

Use any notes you made while observing students work, the students' Math Journal entries, and their written Self-Assessment pieces as further insights into their mathematical thinking.

## About the Interview Assessment Task

Observe pairs as they work during Along the Way. Ask individual students, **How are you working on today's problem?**

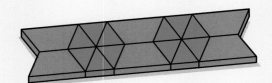

## Possible Responses

We're building the pattern. Every time we put on two red pieces and one green piece, and there are two red pieces on the end.

*Focuses on finding the rule behind the pattern. Is beginning to articulate the rule. (Level 3)*

We're going to trace blocks to make the pattern with ten green gates and see how many blocks that takes. Then we'll figure out how to predict.

*Makes and begins to carry out a plan for finding the rule behind the pattern. (Level 3)*

There's always a green block, then two red blocks, so it takes three blocks for every gate.

*Decides on the rule as he builds the pattern. Neglects to include the first block in the pattern. (Level 2)*

We're building the pattern. This pattern takes four red blocks.

*Builds the pattern and defines a rule for one color. (Level 2)*

## Response Levels

**3** Accomplishes the purposes of the question, task, or unit. Mathematical communication is clear.

**2** Partially accomplishes the purposes of the question, task, or unit. Mathematical communication is somewhat limited.

**1** Shows fragmented understanding. Mathematical communication is vague.

# Week 1
# Red Fences, Green Gates
## Portfolio Review

## Portfolio Review

At the end of this week review each student's work using the guidelines below. Record your findings on a copy of the Performance Observations recording sheet on page 110.

**In the Portfolio:**
- Red Fence, Green Gate recording

What to look for
in the students' work:

- Was the student able to identify patterns?

- Was the student able to identify rules governing patterns?

- Was the student able to use rules to make predictions?

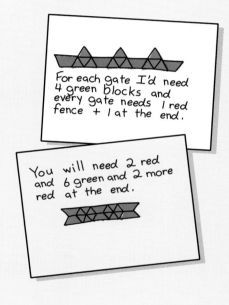

For each gate I'd need 4 green blocks and every gate needs 1 red fence + 1 at the end.

You will need 2 red and 6 green and 2 more red at the end.

## What You Might See

▶ The report and drawings indicate understanding of patterns. Student is able to identify rules and make predictions about patterns. (Level 3)

▶ The report and drawings indicate understanding of patterns. Report draws a few conclusions about numbers of blocks in specific "fences," but student is not able to identify rules or make predictions. (Level 2)

▶ Student draws some of the patterns, but writings do not show any attempt to identify rules or make predictions. (Level 1)

## Week 2
## Rectangle Factory
### Interview Assessment

### About the Interview Assessment Task

As the students work, give individual students a pile of 24 Rainbow Cubes and ask, *How many different rectangles can be made for the number 24?*

### Possible Responses

I know there are 1 x 24, 2 x 12, 3 x 8 and 4 x 6. I can make each rectangle.

*Has a knowledge of the factors of 24 and understands the relationship between them and the rectangles. (Level 3)*

I've made one long rectangle that is 1 row by 24. Now, I'll make 2 rows and see if I can make a rectangle, then 3 rows, then 4 rows.

*Sets up the problem in an orderly and accurate way and comes up with the correct answer. (Level 3)*

I know 2 x 12 = 24, so I can make that rectangle. I also know 8 x 3 = 24, so I can make that rectangle.

*Understands the concept of factors and how they relate to the rectangles, but is less organized and misses some possibilities. (Level 2)*

I can make this rectangle.

*Makes only one rectangle, does not search for other possibilities. (Level 1)*

**Response Levels**

**3** Accomplishes the purposes of the question, task, or unit. Mathematical communication is clear.

**2** Partially accomplishes the purposes of the question, task, or unit. Mathematical communication is somewhat limited.

**1** Shows fragmented understanding. Mathematical communication is vague.

**Week 2
Rectangle Factory
Portfolio Review**

## Portfolio Review

At the end of this week review each student's work using the guidelines below. Record your findings on a copy of the Performance Observations recording sheet on page 110.

**In the Portfolio:**

• Reports on factors, multiples or primes

What to look for
in the students' work:

• **Was it clear what question the report was designed to answer?**

• **Did the student explain how he approached the problem?**

• **Did the student give accurate solutions to and conclusions about the question and explain them?**

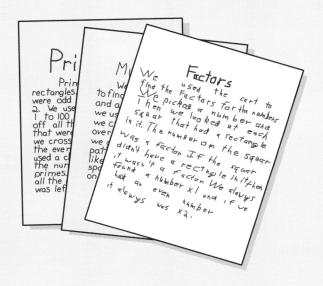

## What You Might See

▶ The question that the student is answering is obvious. The student describes how she approached the question and gives accurate solutions and reasons for them. (Level 3)

▶ The question is displayed clearly. The student tells something about how he approached the question but not how he figured out the answer. Some of the solutions are correct and some are missing. (Level 2)

▶ The report tells which question the student is trying to answer but does not clearly describe how she worked on the problem. Solutions are not given. (Level 1)

# Unit 2
# Looking for Rules
Written Assessment

**Response Levels**

**3** Accomplishes the purposes of the question, task, or unit. Mathematical communication is clear.

**2** Partially accomplishes the purposes of the question, task, or unit. Mathematical communication is somewhat limited.

**1** Shows fragmented understanding. Mathematical communication is vague.

## About the Written Assessment Task

This assessment gives you an opportunity to see students' written responses to a particular question related to the unit. It is not an evaluation of the entire unit. Use this task anytime during the unit or as a pre-unit assessment. You may also use this task with just a few students when you need extra insight into their mathematical thinking.

This assessment task focuses on the students' understanding of pattern and their ability to communicate their ideas clearly.

**Materials:** Each student will need a full sheet of paper.

**Assessment Task:** Ask the students to write in response to the following: *What would you say if you had to explain to a first-grader what "pattern" means?*

## Possible Responses

A pattern is like when you have some cubs or shape it will go

△ ☐ △ ☐ △ ☐

Or you can use letters

A B AB AB

patterns you can see every where.
A patter says something over and over agian
the same thing over and over agian,

◀ Student describes patterns in general, showing clear understanding of pattern. (Level 3)

It's a colors or blockz that repeat it self or, a dezign !

||.||.||.||

△ / ⬡ ⬭ △ / ○

X O X O

☆ A ☆ A

◄ Student describes patterns in general, showing clear understanding of pattern, and gives one or more examples to illustrate. (Level 3)

Student gives examples of patterns but does not describe patterns in general. (Level 2) ►

I would tell a 1st grader what a Padern is by explaining Niceley then drawing a pictur

▮ ▬ ▮ ▬ ▮ ▬

\\ \\ ⁊ ⁊ ⁊ ⁊

| o/o/o /o /o

# Unit 3
# Strategies
## Assessment Overview

## Before the Unit

Several types of assessment are available as you work with your class during this unit:

- Classroom Observations
- Interview Assessments (pages 20, 22, 24, 26, 28)
- Math Journal (Guidebook, pages 60, 69, 77, 83, 93)
- Written Assessment (pages 30, 31)
- Self-Assessment (Guidebook, page 94)
- Portfolio Reviews (pages 21, 23, 25, 27, 29)

The goal is for students to move toward an understanding of the Key Mathematical Ideas and to focus on the Communication Characteristics and Learning Dispositions listed below. Observations, interviews, portfolio materials, and students' self-assessments should all contribute to your overall impression of each student's understanding. It is important to use multiple sources of information to obtain valid inferences of each student's learning over time.

## Use these guidelines as you observe students' work throughout the unit:

| Key Mathematical Ideas | Communication Characteristics | Learning Dispositions |
|---|---|---|
| ★ There are patterns and relationships among multiplication facts that can be useful for memorizing the facts.<br><br>★ Many problems can be solved with mental arithmetic.<br><br>★ The calculator can be a helpful and efficient tool for investigating patterns and solving complex or tedious problems. | ★ Was the student able to explain her ways of solving problems so that they made sense?<br><br>★ Did the student demonstrate fluency in being able to approach the same problem in a variety of ways? | ★ Did the student show perseverance in working toward the solutions of complex problems?<br><br>★ Was the student able to concentrate on committing hard-to-remember number facts to memory? |

You can use this generalized rubric as a suggested guide as you look at students' work and listen to their responses. You may wish to adapt this rubric to make it more task-specific. Share your rubric with your class so that they can take responsibility for monitoring their own learning. ▶

### Response Levels

3 Accomplishes the purposes of the question, task, or unit. Mathematical communication is clear.

2 Partially accomplishes the purposes of the question, task, or unit. Mathematical communication is somewhat limited.

1 Shows fragmented understanding. Mathematical communication is vague.

## After the Unit

Once the class has completed work on this unit, pull together the various pieces listed below and make an overall evaluation of each student's performance. Record your summary on a copy of the Unit Evaluation recording sheet on page 111. You can use the completed Unit Evaluation sheet and the student's portfolio to give family members a picture of their child's progress.

 **Written Assessment**

Strategies Written Assessment, pages 30–31

 **Interview Assessment**

Week 1 • The Multiplication Matrix Interview page 20

Week 2 • Remember This! Interview page 22

Week 3 • Convince Me! Interview page 24

Week 4 • Calculator Investigations Interview page 26

Week 5 • Strategy Show-offs Interview page 28

 **Portfolio Review**

Week 1 • Multiplication Facts Book
page 21 • Multiplication Chart Observations

Week 2 • This Week's Experiences
page 23

Week 3 • Two Problems recordings
page 25

Week 4 • In Five Steps Puzzles
page 27 • Secret Rule recordings

• Digit Possibilities Puzzles

• How Old Am I? recordings

Week 5 • Strategy for Solving a Problem
page 29

Note: In addition to the Portfolio Review work listed here, Home Work and Side Trip work may also have been included in the students' portfolios. See In the Portfolio, Guidebook, page 94.

 **Observation**    **Math Journal**    **Self-Assessment**

Use any notes you made while observing students work, the students' Math Journal entries, and their written Self-Assessment pieces as further insights into their mathematical thinking.

## About the Interview Assessment Task

During Along the Way, ask individual students, *Which fact do you feel most proud of learning this week? What trick did you learn to remember it?*

## Possible Responses

I learned all my nines. I discovered that the answers always add up to nine. They start with one less than the number you're times-ing nine by.

*Student has found a strategy he did not previously know and is using it to remember facts that he previously found difficult to remember. (Level 3)*

I learned 2 x 8 =16. I saw that most times twos were easy. They were just like adding the number twice. So I remember 8 + 8 = 16.

*Student has expanded a strategy that she had previously used, applying it to more facts. (Level 3)*

I remembered that 6 x 6 is 36. I said it to myself so many times that it just sounds right.

*Student remembers a new fact through repetition or sound. (Level 3)*

I didn't learn any new facts this week.

*Student did not add any new facts to the bank of facts she can remember. (Level 1)*

## Portfolio Review

At the end of this week review each student's work using the guidelines below. Record your findings on a copy of the Performance Observations recording sheet on page 110.

### What to look for in the students' work:

- Was the student able to place multiplication rectangles accurately on the chart?

- Was the student able to write out multiplication facts in a facts booklet and indicate which facts he knew and which facts he still needed to learn?

- Was the student able to talk about strategies used for knowing familiar facts?

**In the Portfolio:**
- Multiplication Facts Book
- Multiplication Chart Observations

### What You Might See

▶ Has placed multiplication rectangles accurately on the multiplication chart. Book of Multiplication Facts is complete, with facts that still need to be memorized clearly indicated. Strategies are included for the facts already known. New strategies learned this week are added for the facts not yet known. (Level 3)

▶ Has placed multiplication rectangles accurately on the multiplication chart. Book of Multiplication Facts is complete, although it is not clear what facts the student still needs to learn. Few strategies are included. (Level 2)

▶ Shows some confusion on the multiplication chart, and many rectangles are not placed accurately on the chart. Book of Multiplication Facts is missing several facts. No strategies are included. (Level 1)

## Week 2
## Remember This!
### Interview Assessment

## About the Interview Assessment Task

This week, during which students focus on learning techniques for memorizing facts, is different from any other MathLand week. This assessment also differs from others. It attempts to identify the type of learner the student is: visual or auditory. Students can benefit from gaining awareness of their own best learning styles and understanding how to take advantage of them.

Do not try to assign levels to these responses, but do use any insights you gain to help you adapt material to the styles of different groups of students.

Observe individual students as they engage in the memory activities and games this week. Ask, *What do you do when you try to remember a fact in your mind?*

## Possible Responses

I go like this: 6 x 6 is 36. I listen to the sound in my head.

*Explains using auditory patterns.*

I close my eyes and look at the numbers in my mind.

*Explains using visual techniques.*

I think about it real hard over and over.

*Describes the use of repetition.*

I don't know how I do it.

*Is unable to talk about own thinking.*

## Portfolio Review

 At the end of this week review each student's work using the guidelines below. Record your findings on a copy of the Performance Observations recording sheet on page 110.

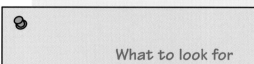

### What to look for in the students' work:

- Did the student participate in each Day Trip game or activity?
- Was the student able to tell about a new strategy for learning multiplication facts?
- Did the student learn new multiplication facts?

**In the Portfolio:**
- This Week's Experiences

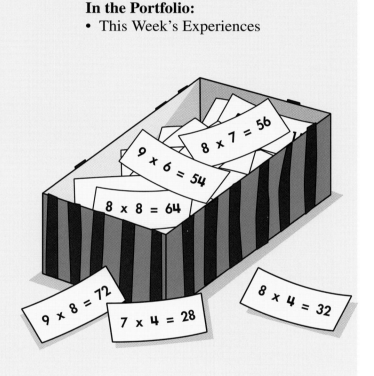

## What You Might See

▶ Has a new strategy for learning multiplication facts and includes several new facts that have been learned. Knows most of the facts. (Level 3)

▶ Has a new strategy for learning multiplication facts and includes some new facts. Has many more facts to commit to memory. (Level 2)

▶ Does not have a new strategy for learning multiplication facts. Has very few of the facts committed to memory. (Level 1)

## About the Interview Assessment Task

As students take part in the discussions this week, pay special attention to the ways they tell how they know. *I'm wondering how you got that answer. Can you convince me that it is right?*

$$35$$
$$\times\ 4$$

142   1220   140

## Possible Responses

I know it's 140, and I can convince you. See, four 30s is 120 and four 5s is 20. That's 140 all together.

*Uses place value to break the problem into parts. Reasons confidently to get the correct answer. (Level 3)*

Well, I'm pretty sure it's 142. Because 4 x 30 is...let's see, 120. Then 4 x 5 is 20, and that's 142 all together.

*Uses correct thinking, but makes an error in computation and is not completely confident. (Level 2)*

I thought it was 1220 because 4 x 5 = 20 and 4 x 3 = 12, but that can't be right. It's way too many.

*Uses incorrect thinking, but realizes error. Needs more chances to develop confidence. (Level 2)*

I said 1220 because 4 x 5 = 20 and 4 x 3 = 12. That's 1220. I don't know any other way to think about it.

*Uses an incorrect version of the standard algorithm. Does not try to approach the problem logically. (Level 1)*

## Portfolio Review

At the end of this week review each student's work using the guidelines below. Record your findings on a copy of the Performance Observations recording sheet on page 110.

**In the Portfolio:**
• Two Problems recording

### What to look for in the students' work:

• Did the student's recording include all of the elements asked for (the problem, the solution, sketches of blocks and a description of how the blocks can be used to prove the solution)?

• How well did the recording communicate the student's thinking?

• Did the recording show a reliance on logical thinking rather than rote procedures?

### What You Might See

▶ Has recordings for several problems and each recording includes all the elements. Problem solutions show good logical thinking. Communication is clear. (Level 3)

▶ Has several recordings and at least one has all the elements, although some recordings are incomplete. Logical thinking is usually evident. Communication sometimes is unclear. (Level 2)

▶ Has only one attempt at a recording, which is incomplete. Descriptions of process are difficult to decipher even by the student. (Level 1)

# UNIT 3

## Week 4
## Calculator Investigations
### Interview Assessment

## About the Interview Assessment Task

As the students work this week, show individual students the three problems below and ask, *For which of these problems would you choose to use the calculator? Why?*

$3 + 8 =$

$30 + 50 + 100 + 2 =$

$356 \times 78 =$

## Possible Responses

*I would choose to do 356 x 78, because I can do the other problems in my head faster.*

Chooses a problem that is difficult to figure out with mental arithmetic. Reason to use calculator is related to own abilities and the unique qualities of the calculator. (Level 3)

*I would choose to do 356 x 78, because I can't do it.*

Reason for choosing a problem is based on lack of confidence in own ability to solve the problem because it is too difficult, rather than on the amount of time the problem would take to solve without a calculator. (Level 2)

*I would choose to do 30 + 50 + 100 + 2, because it has the most numbers.*

Chooses the problem that appears to be most lengthy even though it is actually fairly easy. May be choosing without reflection. (Level 2)

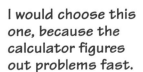

*I would choose this one, because the calculator figures out problems fast.*

Chooses a problem at random. Even with further questioning, it is clear that the student thinks that choosing a calculator is always the best solution. (Level 1)

## Response Levels

**3** *Accomplishes the purposes of the question, task, or unit. Mathematical communication is clear.*

**2** *Partially accomplishes the purposes of the question, task, or unit. Mathematical communication is somewhat limited.*

**1** *Shows fragmented understanding. Mathematical communication is vague.*

## Portfolio Review

 At the end of this week review each student's work using the guidelines below. Record your findings on a copy of the Performance Observations recording sheet on page 110.

### What to look for in the students' work:

- Did the student complete a recording for each Day Trip?
- Was the student able to enter keystrokes accurately?
- Do the recordings indicate understanding of appropriate key strokes?

### In the Portfolio:
- In Five Steps Puzzle
- Secret Rule recording
- Digit Possibilities Puzzle
- How Old Am I? recording

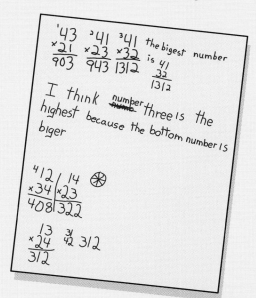

## What You Might See

▶ Includes recordings for each Day Trip. All of the recordings demonstrate accuracy and an understanding of the keystrokes needed to perform appropriate computations. (Level 3)

▶ Includes recordings for each Day Trip. Most of the recordings demonstrate the ability to enter keystrokes accurately and some understanding of the appropriate keystrokes. (Level 2)

▶ Several of the recordings from the week are missing. Of the recordings available, most indicate confusion about the appropriate keystrokes. (Level 1)

**Response Levels**

**3** Accomplishes the purposes of the question, task, or unit. Mathematical communication is clear.

**2** Partially accomplishes the purposes of the question, task, or unit. Mathematical communication is somewhat limited.

**1** Shows fragmented understanding. Mathematical communication is vague.

## About the Interview Assessment Task

As the students are working this week, ask individual students, **What strategies are you using to solve the problem you are working on?**

**Possible Responses**

I'm trying to figure out how to arrange the digits 2, 4, 6, 8 to equal 3772. I'm estimating and trying out my ideas on my calculator, because I can do it quickest that way.

*Explains strategies and realizes that the calculator is the most efficient tool for the specific problem. (Level 3)*

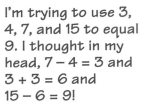

I'm trying to use 3, 4, 7, and 15 to equal 9. I thought in my head, 7 − 4 = 3 and 3 + 3 = 6 and 15 − 6 = 9!

*Explains an efficient mental arithmetic strategy. (Level 3)*

I'm trying to multiply 32 and 12 in my mind. I know that 30 x 10 is 300 and 2 x 2 is 4. I think the answer should be 304, but when I do it with a calculator I get 384. I'm not sure what the right answer is.

*Explains a strategy that does not work because it is incomplete. (Level 2)*

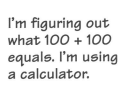

I'm figuring out what 100 + 100 equals. I'm using a calculator.

*Explains a strategy that works but is clearly less-efficient than another strategy. (Level 2)*

## Response Levels

**3** Accomplishes the purposes of the question, task, or unit. Mathematical communication is clear.

**2** Partially accomplishes the purposes of the question, task, or unit. Mathematical communication is somewhat limited.

**1** Shows fragmented understanding. Mathematical communication is vague.

**Week 5**
## Strategy Show-off
Portfolio Review

## Portfolio Review

At the end of this week review each student's work using the guidelines below. Record your findings on a copy of the Performance Observations recording sheet on page 110.

**In the Portfolio:**
- Strategy for Solving a Problem

### What to look for in the students' work:

- Was the student able to find different ways to represent the same number with Base Ten Blocks?
- Was the student able to use arithmetic strategies to play card games?
- Was the student able to arrange given digits to make a true multiplication equation for a certain answer?

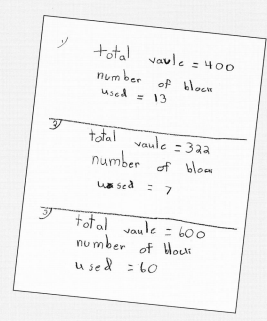

## What You Might See

▶ Recordings show a clear understanding of many different ways to represent numbers using Base Ten Blocks. Student readily used mental arithmetic strategies efficiently to play card games. Portfolio includes several recordings of true multiplication equations using a given set of digits. (Level 3)

▶ Recordings show an understanding of some different ways to represent numbers using Base Ten Blocks. Student occasionally used mental arithmetic strategies to play card games. Portfolio includes some recordings of true multiplication equations using a given set of digits. (Level 2)

▶ Recordings do not show an understanding of different ways to represent numbers using Base Ten Blocks. Student was unable to use mental arithmetic strategies efficiently to play card games. Includes only one or two recordings of multiplication equations using a given set of digits. (Level 1)

# Unit 3
# Strategies
## Written Assessment

**Response Levels**

**3** Accomplishes the purposes of the question, task, or unit. Mathematical communication is clear.

**2** Partially accomplishes the purposes of the question, task, or unit. Mathematical communication is somewhat limited.

**1** Shows fragmented understanding. Mathematical communication is vague.

## About the Written Assessment Task

This assessment gives you an opportunity to see students' written responses to a particular question related to the unit. It is not an evaluation of the entire unit. Use this task anytime during the unit or as a pre-unit assessment. You may also use this task with just a few students when you need extra insight into their mathematical thinking.

This assessment task focuses on students' understandings of multiplication by attempting to determine what facts they know and what mental images and constructs they have for multiplication.

**Materials:** Each student will need a full sheet of paper.

**Assessment Task:** Have the students write in response to the following: *Write what you know about multiplication. Write some multiplication facts you know and some harder multiplication problems you can do.*

## Possible Responses

I think that multiplication is easier because you dont always have to add or devide because like if you say 4 x9 then you don't have to do this so you could tak less time doing your multiplication facts. Multiplacation facts are much faster so I think you should use Multiplacation.

| 3 ×6 = 18 | 4 ×3 = 12 | 9 ×5 = 45 | 7 ×2 = 14 | 8 ×9 = 72 | 1 ×0 = 0 | 5 ×3 = 15 | 6 ×3 = 18 | 3 ×3 = 9 |

| 9 ×9 = 81 | 6 ×5 = 30 | 4 ×5 = 20 | 3 ×9 = 27 | 7 ×9 = 63 | 3 ×7 = 21 | 5 ×2 = 10 |

$$1{,}034{,}210 \times 3 = 3{,}102{,}630$$

$$257{,}320 \times 5 = 1{,}286{,}600$$

◄ Student gives at least one description of what multiplication is, several multiplication facts, and also a couple of more difficult multiplication problems. Student obviously understands quite a bit about multiplication. (Level 3)

**Response Levels**

**3** Accomplishes the purposes of the question, task, or unit. Mathematical communication is clear.

**2** Partially accomplishes the purposes of the question, task, or unit. Mathematical communication is somewhat limited.

**1** Shows fragmented understanding. Mathematical communication is vague.

I Know that multiplication is a quiker way to add like you have 1 box of apples then in that box there is 10 apples. You are going to multiply 1 times 10. That is a quicker way to do that instead of adding.

2: 5×3=15, 6×9=54, 3×4=12, 9×8=72, 9×3=27, 2×9=18, 5×5=25, 3×8=24, 8×7=56

3: John had $20 dollars he bought 10 marbels that it cost $7. How much money does John has?

$20
- 7
$13

◀ Student work shows evidence of familiarity with the concept of multiplication, but examples of multiplication facts or problems do not demonstrate the concept is fully understood. (Level 2)

Student knows some multiplication facts and tries to describe what multiplication is. (Level 2) ▶

Multiplication is a tipe of math that can be eazyer in some formes of your life.

① 1×20=20
② 2×10=20
③ 3×4=12
④ 4×8=32
⑤ 5×10=50
⑥ 50×2=100
⑦ 10×100=1000
⑧ 40×2=80
⑨ 50×100=5000
⑩ 3×400=1200

## Before the Unit

Several types of assessment are available as you work with your class during this unit:
- Classroom Observations
- Interview Assessments (pages 34, 36)
- Math Journal (Guidebook, page 109)
- Written Assessment (pages 38–39)
- Self-Assessment (Guidebook, page 118)
- Portfolio Reviews (pages 35, 37)

The goal is for students to move toward an understanding of the Key Mathematical Ideas and to focus on the Communication Characteristics and Learning Dispositions listed below. Observations, interviews, portfolio materials, and students' self-assessments should all contribute to your overall impression of each student's understanding. It is important to use multiple sources of information to obtain valid inferences of each student's learning over time.

**Use these guidelines as you observe students' work throughout the unit:**

| Key Mathematical Ideas | Communication Characteristics | Learning Dispositions |
| --- | --- | --- |
| ★ The attributes of a collection of shapes can be the basis of a system of organization for those shapes. <br><br> ★ Shapes can be compared by considering differences as well as likenesses. <br><br> ★ The solution to a permutation or combination problem consists of all of the possible unique ways to satisfy the problem conditions. | ★ How organized and complete were the student's recordings and descriptions of the unit's work? <br><br> ★ How fluent was the student in identifying solutions? | ★ Did the student show perseverance and flexibility of thinking when working on the tasks in this unit? <br><br> ★ Was the student able to use patterns as a strategy for finding solution sets? |

You can use this generalized rubric as a suggested guide as you look at students' work and listen to their responses. You may wish to adapt this rubric to make it more task-specific. Share your rubric with your class so that they can take responsibility for monitoring their own learning. ▶

**Response Levels**

3  Accomplishes the purposes of the question, task, or unit. Mathematical communication is clear.

2  Partially accomplishes the purposes of the question, task, or unit. Mathematical communication is somewhat limited.

1  Shows fragmented understanding. Mathematical communication is vague.

## After the Unit

Once the class has completed work on this unit, pull together the various pieces listed below and make an overall evaluation of each student's performance. Record your summary on a copy of the Unit Evaluation recording sheet on page 111. You can use the completed Unit Evaluation sheet and the student's portfolio to give family members a picture of their child's progress.

 **Written Assessment**

That's Unique Written Assessment, pages 38–39

 **Interview Assessment**

Week 1 • Detecting Differences Interview
page 34

Week 2 • Think of the Possibilities! Interview
page 36

 **Portfolio Review**

Week 1 • Attribute Set Organizational
page 35    Diagram
        • Difference Dividend recordings

Week 2 • Towers of Three recordings
page 37 • Tower Construction Rules and
         Solutions
        • Balance Scale recordings
        • QuadraCube recordings

Note: In addition to the Portfolio Review work listed here, Home Work and Side Trip work may also have been included in the students' portfolios. See In the Portfolio, Guidebook, page 118.

 **Observation**     **Math Journal**     **Self-Assessment**

Use any notes you made while observing students work, the students' Math Journal entries, and their written Self-Assessment pieces as further insights into their mathematical thinking.

*Response Levels*

**3** Accomplishes the purposes of the question, task, or unit. Mathematical communication is clear.

**2** Partially accomplishes the purposes of the question, task, or unit. Mathematical communication is somewhat limited.

**1** Shows fragmented understanding. Mathematical communication is vague.

## About the Interview Assessment Task

As the students work this week, show individual students one attribute piece and say, ***Find a piece that is different from this piece in only two ways. Tell me how it's different.***

## Possible Responses

This one's different in shape and color. And this one's different in size and shape.

*Identifies several pieces that differ in exactly two ways and tells how they differ. (Level 3)*

This one's different in two ways. It's the same color, but it's a different size and a different shape.

*Identifies an appropriate piece and clearly explains the differences. (Level 3)*

How about this one? It's a different color and shape. Oops! It's a different size, too. Never mind. I'll pick this piece instead.

*Selects inappropriate piece, then revises choice to appropriate piece. (Level 3)*

This one's a different shape and color.

*Selects a piece that's different in three ways, but tells two of three ways. (Level 2)*

## Portfolio Review

 At the end of this week review each student's work using the guidelines below. Record your findings on a copy of the Performance Observations recording sheet on page 110.

**In the Portfolio:**
- Attribute Set Organizational Diagram
- Difference Dividend recording

### What to look for in the students' work:

- Was the student able to organize the attribute pieces in some logical way?

- Was the student able to identify and communicate differences among the attribute pieces?

- How well do the student's recordings convey the logical thought that went into the work?

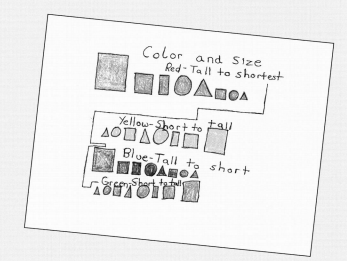

## What You Might See

▶ Organization of attribute set is clear and well-explained. Approach to finding differences among pieces is logically-organized. (Level 3)

▶ Day Trip One recording shows attribute set organized by one attribute; there is no systematic organization by second and third attribute. Description is somewhat unclear. Day Trip Five recording indicates that the student usually considers all three variables, but does not always identify correct number of differences. (Level 2)

▶ Recording shows a random arrangement of attribute set, with some pieces missing or duplicated. No written explanation about the set's organization is given. More often than not, student is unable to detect or describe differences between pieces in the set. (Level 1)

**Response Levels**

**3** Accomplishes the purposes of the question, task, or unit. Mathematical communication is clear.

**2** Partially accomplishes the purposes of the question, task, or unit. Mathematical communication is somewhat limited.

**1** Shows fragmented understanding. Mathematical communication is vague.

## About the Interview Assessment Task

During Along the Way, as pairs begin work on the problem of the day, say to individual students, **Tell me how you are going about solving this problem.**

## Possible Responses

I'm going to make a list. I'll start with blue cubes on the bottom and find all those towers, then I'll do green cubes on the bottom....

*Decides on an organized approach before working on the problem. (Level 3)*

I was just writing down every solution I could think of but I was getting repeats. So I started over and now all the ones that start the same will go together.

*Searches for solutions randomly at first, then reorganizes to use a more strategic approach. (Level 3)*

I just write down whatever I think of that works.

*Uses a random approach throughout the solution search. Finds most solutions. (Level 2)*

Well, I got these three, but I can't think of any more.

*Proceeds randomly and finds only a few solutions. (Level 1)*

| Response Levels | | Week 2 |  |
|---|---|---|---|

**Response Levels**

**3** Accomplishes the purposes of the question, task, or unit. Mathematical communication is clear.

**2** Partially accomplishes the purposes of the question, task, or unit. Mathematical communication is somewhat limited.

**1** Shows fragmented understanding. Mathematical communication is vague.

## Week 2
## Think of the Possibilities!
### Portfolio Review

## Portfolio Review

At the end of this week review each student's work using the guidelines below. Record your findings on a copy of the Performance Observations recording sheet on page 110.

What to look for
in the students' work:

- How complete was the recorded solution set for each day's problem?
- Were the solutions organized in a systematic way?
- Were the recordings clear and easy to follow?

**In the Portfolio:**
- Towers of Three recording
- Tower Construction Rules and Solutions
- Balance Scale recording
- QuadraCube recording

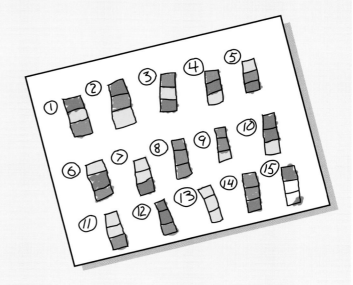

## What You Might See

▶ Recordings show complete, logically-organized solution sets for most Day Trips. Sets are clear and easy to follow. (Level 3)

▶ Recordings show many solutions to each day's problem and are sometimes confusing and difficult to decipher. By end of week, a more organized approach to the solution search becomes evident. (Level 2)

▶ Does not have a recording for each day's work. Recordings available show only a minimum number of possible solutions, gathered without apparent attempt at organization. (Level 1)

# Unit 4
# That's Unique
## Written Assessment

## About the Written Assessment Task

This assessment gives you an opportunity to see students' responses to a particular question related to the unit. It is not an evaluation of the entire unit. Use this task anytime during the unit or as a pre-unit assessment. You may also use this task with just a few students when you need extra insight into their mathematical thinking.

This assessment task focuses on the ability to use a systematic approach to a combinations problem.

**Materials:** Each student will need a full sheet of paper.

**Assessment Task:** Ask the students, *How many different ways can you arrange the digits 1, 2, 3, and 4 to make a four-digit number, using each digit only once in a number? Record the numbers you make. Write about how you organized your work, and tell of any patterns you used.*

(Note: There are 24 ways:

| | | | |
|------|------|------|------|
| 1234 | 2134 | 3124 | 4123 |
| 1243 | 2143 | 3142 | 4132 |
| 1324 | 2314 | 3214 | 4213 |
| 1342 | 2341 | 3241 | 4231 |
| 1423 | 2413 | 3412 | 4312 |
| 1432 | 2431 | 3421 | 4321) |

## Possible Responses

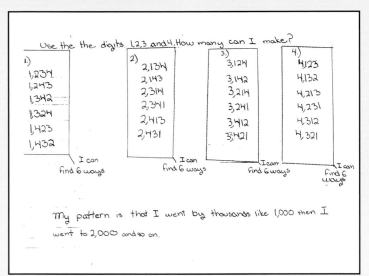

◀ Uses a systematic approach to find all 24 possibilities. Written explanation describes an organized problem-solving strategy. (Level 3)

Use the digits 1, 2, 3, and 4
How many 4 digit numbers
can I make?

① 4,123
② 3,412
③ 2,341
④ 1,234
⑤ 1,324
⑥ 2,431
⑦ 3,124
⑧ 4,231
⑨ 2,314
⑩ 3,214
⑪ 1,423
⑫ 4,312
⑬ 3,421
⑭ 4,321
⑮ 3,241
⑯ 1,432
⑰ 1,342
⑱ 2,134
⑲ 2,413
⑳ 3,142

I found a pattern in the first four numbers. The pattern is at the end of each of these four digit numbers is the number that is suppose to come before the first number.

◀ Finds almost all of the 24 possibilities. Begins solution search randomly, then discovers a pattern and proceeds in a more organized manner. Explanation of pattern is fairly clear. (Level 2)

Finds only a few of the 24 possibilities. Solution set includes duplicates. Uses a seemingly random approach. Explanation does not mention patterns or organized strategies. (Level 1)  ▶

Use the digits 1, 2, 3, and 4
How many 4 digit numbers can I make?

| | | | |
|---|---|---|---|
| 1,2,3,4 | 2,431 | 4,132 | 1,324 |
| 2,1,3,4, | 3,142 | 2,134 | 1,423 |
| 3,2,1,4 | 3,241 | 3,421 | |
| 4,321 | | | 1,432 |
| 3,241 | 1,213 | | |
| 4,213 | 2,431 | 2,134 | 2,341 |
| 1,324 | 2,341 | 3,421 | |
| 1,243 | 2,314 | 1,243 | |
| 4,231 | 4213 | 1,342 | |
| 1,423 | 3,124 | 1,243 | |
| 1,432 | 4,123 | 2,134 | |
| 2,314 | 3,214 | 4,132 | |
| 2,413 | 4,231 | 2,143 | |
| 1,431 | 2,143B | | |

I do not think I have a pattern.

## Before the Unit

Several types of assessment are available as you work with your class during this unit:

- Classroom Observations
- Interview Assessments (pages 42, 44, 46, 48, 50)
- Math Journal (Guidebook, pages 129, 149, 153, 161)
- Written Assessment, pages 52–53
- Self-Assessment (Guidebook, page 166)
- Portfolio Reviews (pages 43, 45, 47, 49, 51)

The goal is for students to move toward an understanding of the Key Mathematical Ideas and to focus on the Communication Characteristics and Learning Dispositions listed below. Observations, interviews, portfolio materials, and students' self-assessments should all contribute to your overall impression of each student's understanding. It is important to use multiple sources of information to obtain valid inferences of each student's learning over time.

### Use these guidelines as you observe students' work throughout the unit:

| Key Mathematical Ideas | Communication Characteristics | Learning Dispositions |
|---|---|---|
| ★ When a whole is broken up into equal parts, each part is a fraction of the whole.<br><br>★ The size of the fractional part is dependent on the size of the whole.<br><br>★ Any fraction can be named in many different, equivalent ways.<br><br>★ Addition and subtraction equations are another way of showing equivalence with fractions. | ★ Was the student organized in working on problems?<br><br>★ Did the student show the ability to make sense of new information when working on the tasks in this unit? | ★ Did the student show confidence in applying new learning?<br><br>★ Did the student show concentration in pursuing the investigations in this unit? |

You can use this generalized rubric as a suggested guide as you look at students' work and listen to their responses. You may wish to adapt this rubric to make it more task-specific. Share your rubric with your class so that they can take responsibility for monitoring their own learning.

**Response Levels**

3 Accomplishes the purposes of the question, task, or unit. Mathematical communication is clear.

2 Partially accomplishes the purposes of the question, task, or unit. Mathematical communication is somewhat limited.

1 Shows fragmented understanding. Mathematical communication is vague.

## After the Unit

Once the class has completed work on this unit, pull together the various pieces listed below and make an overall evaluation of each student's performance. Record your summary on a copy of the Unit Evaluation recording sheet on page 111. You can use the completed Unit Evaluation sheet and the student's portfolio to give family members a picture of their child's progress.

 **Written Assessment**

Numbers Between Numbers Written Assessment, pages 52–53

 **Interview Assessment**

Week 1 • It's All Relative Interview
page 42

Week 2 • Close-up on Fraction Circles
page 44    Interview

Week 3 • Can You Make? Questions
page 46    Interview

Week 4 • Fractions Plus and Minus Interview
page 48

Week 5 • Fraction Cafe Interview
page 50

 **Portfolio Review**

Week 1 • 24 Raisins recording
page 43 • Fraction Puzzles
        • Which Is Greater? questions

Week 2 • What Fraction Is That? recordings
page 45 • Name that Fraction recordings
        • Fraction Folding recordings

Week 3 • *Can You Make?* Posters
page 47 • *Are There More Ways to Equal $\frac{1}{2}$ or $\frac{1}{3}$?* recordings

Week 4 • True Equations lists
page 49 • Fraction Puzzles Strategy recordings

Week 5 • Fraction Café Problem Solutions
page 51 • Fraction Problems

Note: In addition to the Portfolio Review work listed here, Home Work and Side Trip work may also have been included in the students' portfolios. See In the Portfolio, Guidebook, page 166.

 **Observation**     **Math Journal**     **Self-Assessment**

Use any notes you made while observing students work, the students' Math Journal entries, and their written Self-Assessment pieces as further insights into their mathematical thinking.

# Week 1
## It's All Relative
### Interview Assessment

## About the Interview Assessment Task

As the students are working this week, approach individual students and ask, *What fraction are you showing now? How are you showing it?*

## Possible Responses

We're showing $\frac{1}{4}$. We broke a quarter off this cracker and put it next to the rest of it. We made a shape with 4 triangles and pushed one away. And we put out 8 cubes and pushed 2 away. That's $\frac{1}{4}$.

*Shows clear understanding of the concept of fractions. Each representation clearly represents the appropriate fraction. Fractional parts of a set are included. (Level 3)*

We're showing $\frac{1}{2}$. We filled a cup half full of water, and cut a marshmallow in half, and broke a cracker in half.

*Shows clear understanding of the concept of fractions. Each representation clearly represents the appropriate fraction. (Level 3)*

We're showing $\frac{1}{2}$. See, here's $\frac{1}{2}$ a cracker, $\frac{1}{2}$ a piece of bread, and $\frac{1}{2}$ a marshmallow.

*Shows some understanding of the concept of fractions, but some items in display are not divided into equal parts. (Level 2)*

We're showing $\frac{1}{4}$. See, here are 4 cubes, and here are 4 crackers, and here are 4 pieces of bread.

*Does not show understanding of the concept of fractions. Rather than showing a fraction, shows the whole number in its denominator. (Level 1)*

## Portfolio Review

At the end of this week review each student's work using the guidelines below. Record your findings on a copy of the Performance Observations recording sheet on page 110.

**What to look for
in the students' work:**

- Was the student able to make a recording showing the number 24 split into various fractional parts?

- Was the student able to make a Fraction Puzzle with a variety of representations of a fractional number, and include one representation that does not belong?

- Do the student's answers to the "Which Is Greater?" questions indicate understanding of the relativity of a fraction's size?

**In the Portfolio:**

- 24 Raisins recording
- Fraction Puzzle
- Which is Greater? questions

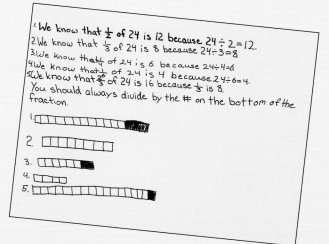

## What You Might See

▶ 24 Raisins recording shows clear understanding of fractional parts of the set. Fraction Puzzle includes a variety of representations of a fraction and includes one example that does not belong. Answers to Which Is Greater? questions indicate understanding of the relativity of a fraction's size. (Level 3)

▶ 24 Raisins recording shows understanding of $\frac{1}{2}$ but confusion about other fractional parts. In Fraction Puzzle it is not clear which example doesn't belong. Answers to Which Is Greater? questions indicate some understanding of the relativity of a fraction's size. (Level 2)

▶ 24 Raisins recording shows confusion about fractional parts of the set. Fraction Puzzle has representations of a whole number rather than a fraction. Answers to Which Is Greater? questions indicate confusion about the relativity of a fraction's size. (Level 1)

# UNIT 5

## Week 2
## Close-up on Fraction Circles
### Interview Assessment

## About the Interview Assessment Task

As the students work with their fraction pieces, point to one piece and ask individual students, *What fraction is this? How many of these do you need to make a whole circle? How do you know?*

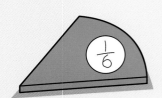

## Possible Responses:

That piece is one sixth. It takes 6 of them to make a whole circle. I know because the name of the fraction tells how many pieces the whole is divided into.

*Confidently gives the fraction name. Makes the connection between the language used to name the fraction piece and what it tells about the whole. (Level 3)*

One sixth. Six sixths make a whole circle. I just know it. I don't know how to explain it.

*Is able to name the fraction piece and identify the number of that fraction needed to make a whole, but is unable to offer an explanation. (Level 2)*

It's one sixth. If I could just find all the pieces I would know how many. I think I found them all now. There are 6 pieces in that color, so it takes 6 to make the whole circle.

*Relies on visual clues rather than on the meaning of the fraction to identify the number of pieces required to make a whole. (Level 2)*

It says one on top of six. I don't know how many pieces would make a whole circle.

*Does not use conventional math language to name the fractional part. Is unable to tell the number of pieces it would take to make a whole circle. (Level 1)*

## Portfolio Review

 At the end of this week review each student's work using the guidelines below. Record your findings on a copy of the Performance Observations recording sheet on page 110.

**What to look for in the students' work:**

- Was the student able to organize and sketch the set of Fraction Circles?

- Was the student able to use fraction notation to identify fractions with numerators greater than 1?

- Did the student find other ways to name $\frac{1}{2}$ and $\frac{1}{3}$?

- Was the student able to describe strategies for folding paper into fractional parts?

**In the Portfolio:**
- What Fraction Is That? recording
- Name That Fraction recording
- Fraction Folding recording

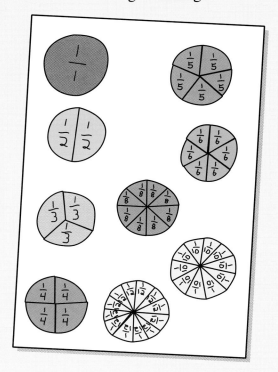

## What You Might See

▶ Student organizes and sketches the Fraction Circles in a way that demonstrates understanding of the sequence of fractions. Answer sheet for Name that Fraction indicates understanding of fraction notation. Is able to find several different ways to name $\frac{1}{2}$ and $\frac{1}{3}$. (Level 3)

▶ Student sketches Fraction Circles with some difficulty, and sketches lack apparent organization. Answer sheet for Name that Fraction shows some confusion about how to write fraction notation for fractions with numerators greater than 1. Is able to find some ways to name $\frac{1}{2}$ and $\frac{1}{3}$. (Level 2)

▶ Student sketches only a few Fraction Circles and does not organize them in a meaningful way. Answer sheet for Name that Fraction reveals lack of understanding of conventional fraction naming and notation. Is unable to find ways to name $\frac{1}{2}$ and $\frac{1}{3}$. (Level 1)

## Week 3
## Can You Make? Questions
### Interview Assessment

## About the Interview Assessment Task

While the class is working during Along the Way, ask individual students, *What question are you exploring now? Is your answer yes or no? Tell me about your thinking.*

## Possible Responses

Can you make $\frac{1}{2}$ with twelfths? I'm pretty sure, because we already made $\frac{1}{2}$ with 2 fourths. I'll know for sure just as soon as I finish putting the twelfths pieces on top of the $\frac{1}{2}$ piece.

*Uses developing sense of fraction equivalence as well as Fraction Circles to formulate and support answer. (Level 3)*

Can you make $\frac{1}{3}$ with eighths is what we're trying to do. I can't tell until I put the pieces together. No, it won't work because 2 eighths is too small and 3 eighths is too big.

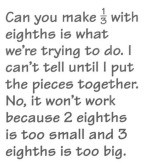

*Relies on visual relationship of Fraction Circles to determine equivalence. (Level 3)*

I'm trying to make $\frac{1}{4}$ with twelfths. These 2 twelfths don't cover enough of the $\frac{1}{4}$, so I guess you can't make $\frac{1}{4}$ with twelfths.

*Method of determining equivalence by comparing Fraction Circles is reliable, but exploration is not complete. (Level 2)*

The question I'm thinking of is, Can you make $\frac{1}{2}$ with tenths? I can't tell for sure. Maybe.

*Method of determining equivalence is not very reliable. Has difficulty drawing a conclusion about equivalence. (Level 1)*

**Week 3**
**Can You Make? Questions**
Portfolio Review

## Portfolio Review

At the end of this week review each student's work using the guidelines below. Record your findings on a copy of the Performance Observations recording sheet on page 110.

### What to look for in the students' work:

- Was the student able to determine whether one fraction could be made with another?

- Was the student able to formulate *Can you make?* questions and find the answers?

- Was the student able to determine whether there are more ways to make $\frac{1}{2}$ or $\frac{1}{3}$?

**In the Portfolio:**
- *Can You Make?* Poster
- Are There More Ways to Equal $\frac{1}{2}$ or $\frac{1}{3}$? recording

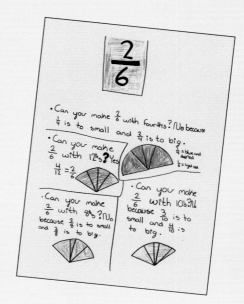

## What You Might See

▶ Uses Fraction Circles to determine whether one fraction can be made with another and supports resulting conclusion. Fluently formulates *Can you make?* questions, explores possibilities, and draws conclusions which are supported with sketches and writing. Thoroughly explores the different ways to make $\frac{1}{2}$ and $\frac{1}{3}$ and comes to a conclusion based on findings. (Level 3)

▶ Uses Fraction Circles to explore whether a fraction can be made with another fraction and usually supports resulting conclusion. Formulates *Can you make?* questions, but some conclusions are incorrect and lack sketches and written statements supporting them. Finds several ways to make $\frac{1}{2}$ and $\frac{1}{3}$, but does not find enough ways to draw a valid conclusion. (Level 2)

▶ Has difficulty determining whether one fraction can be made with another, and conclusions seem to be based on guessing. Has some difficulty formulating and exploring questions on own. Creates only a few incomplete posters. Finds only a few different ways to make $\frac{1}{2}$ and $\frac{1}{3}$ before giving up. (Level 1)

## About the Interview Assessment Task

As the students work during Along the Way, show individual students an equation strip for $\frac{1}{6} + \frac{1}{2} = \frac{4}{6}$, and ask, *Is this equation true or false? How do you know?*

## Possible Responses

I know that $\frac{1}{2}$ is the same as $\frac{3}{6}$ because I remember that from what we did before. And $\frac{3}{6}$ added to $\frac{1}{6}$ is $\frac{4}{6}$. I don't even need to use the fraction pieces to know it's true.

*Confidently uses knowledge of equivalent fractions to determine that $\frac{1}{6} + \frac{1}{2} = \frac{4}{6}$ is true. (Level 3)*

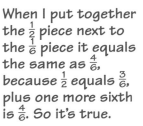

When I put together the $\frac{1}{2}$ piece next to the $\frac{1}{6}$ piece it equals the same as $\frac{4}{6}$, because $\frac{1}{2}$ equals $\frac{3}{6}$, plus one more sixth is $\frac{4}{6}$. So it's true.

*Uses fraction pieces to determine that $\frac{1}{6} + \frac{1}{2} = \frac{4}{6}$ is true. (Level 3)*

Well, here's the $\frac{1}{2}$ piece and the $\frac{1}{6}$ piece. And here I made $\frac{4}{6}$ together, but I can't tell if it's true or false.

*Uses fraction pieces to show $\frac{1}{2} + \frac{1}{6}$, but is unable to determine whether it is equal to $\frac{4}{6}$. (Level 2)*

I found the $\frac{1}{2}$ and the $\frac{1}{6}$. But they're not the same color, so I don't know what to call them when they get put together. I think it's false.

*Does not apply concept of equivalence to addition. (Level 1)*

## Portfolio Review

 At the end of this week review each student's work using the guidelines below. Record your findings on a copy of the Performance Observations recording sheet on page 110.

**In the Portfolio:**
- True Equations list
- Fraction Puzzles Strategy recording

### What to look for in the students' work:

- Was the student able to find equivalent fractions?
- Was the student able to write addition equations to express equivalent fractions?
- Was the student able to use visualization and logical thinking to think about fraction addition equations?

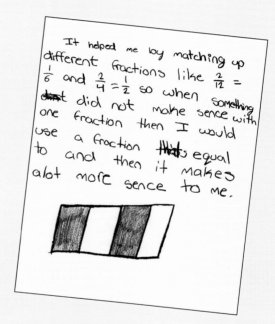

## What You Might See

▶ Finds and records several true addition and subtraction equations involving like and unlike denominators. Demonstrates visualization skills and logical-thinking skills when solving the fraction-addition equation puzzles. (Level 3)

▶ Finds and records several true addition and subtraction equations, but records as true some equations that are false. Needs to use fraction pieces to solve many, but not all, of the cut-apart equation puzzles. (Level 2)

▶ Many equations listed as "true" equations are actually false. When queried, student cannot explain or show why the equations are true. Has difficulty solving the equation puzzles, even using the fraction pieces. (Level 1)

## About the Interview Assessment Task

Approach pairs as they work this week and say to individual students, ***Tell me another name for*** $\frac{7}{2}$. ***Draw a picture of what*** $\frac{7}{2}$ ***looks like.***

## Possible Responses

Here's 7 halves. Two halves make 1. So that's 1, 2, 3, and $\frac{1}{2}$.

*Writes out 7 halves and indicates that 2 halves equal 1, so that the answer is 3 $\frac{1}{2}$. (Level 3)*

That's 7 halves. If you put 7 halves together you get 3 wholes and 1 half.

*Draws a picture showing 7 half fraction circles. Clearly indicates that 7 halves equals 3 $\frac{1}{2}$. (Level 3)*

Here's 7 halves.

*Draws a picture showing 7 half fraction circles, but is unable to determine that it is equivalent to 3 $\frac{1}{2}$. (Level 2)*

Here are 7 twos. That's 14.

*Draws a picture of 7 groups of two. Says that 7 halves is equal to 14. (Level 1)*

## Portfolio Review

At the end of this week review each student's work using the guidelines below. Record your findings on a copy of the Performance Observations recording sheet on page 110.

**What to look for in the students' work:**

- Did the student complete a recording for each Fraction Cafe Problem?

- Does each recording indicate an ability to think about fractions and choose a strategy to solve a problem involving fractions?

- Can each recording be interpreted by someone other than the student?

**In the Portfolio:**
- Fraction Cafe Problem Solutions
- Fraction Problems

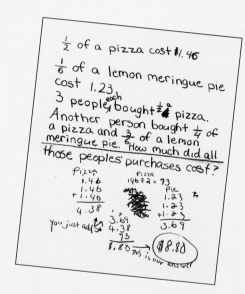

## What You Might See

▶ Includes recordings for each Fraction Cafe Problem. All recordings can be interpreted easily and indicate an ability to approach a fraction problem with understanding. (Level 3)

▶ Includes recordings for each Fraction Cafe Problem. Although some recordings are difficult to interpret, most indicate some ability to approach fraction problems. (Level 2)

▶ Includes only one or two recordings from the week. Most of the recordings are difficult to interpret and show little understanding of fractions. (Level 1)

## About the Written Assessment Task

This assessment gives you an opportunity to see students' written responses to a particular question related to the unit. It is not an evaluation of the entire unit. Use this task anytime during the unit or as a pre-unit assessment. You may also use this task with just a few students when you need extra insight into their mathematical thinking.

This assessment task focuses on students' understanding of fractional parts of a whole.

**Materials:** Each student will need a full sheet of paper.

**Assessment Task:** Present the following to the students: Which is greater, $\frac{4}{4}$ *or* $\frac{5}{5}$? *Draw pictures and use words to tell about your thinking.*

## Possible Responses

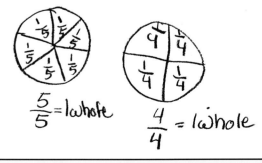

◀ Student determines that $\frac{4}{4}$ and $\frac{5}{5}$ are equal because $\frac{4}{4}$ is equal to one whole and $\frac{5}{5}$ is equal to one whole. (Level 3)

### Response Levels

**3** Accomplishes the purposes of the question, task, or unit. Mathematical communication is clear.

**2** Partially accomplishes the purposes of the question, task, or unit. Mathematical communication is somewhat limited.

**1** Shows fragmented understanding. Mathematical communication is vague.

I think that 4/4 is greater than 5/5 because in fractions the lower the # gets bigger the higher it goes it gets smallar

  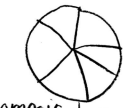

compair $\frac{1}{4}$ v.s. $\frac{1}{5}$

◀ Student reasons that $\frac{4}{4}$ is greater than $\frac{5}{5}$, because fourths are bigger than fifths. (Level 2)

Student does not understand what fourths and fifths are, but decides that fives are greater than fours. (Level 1)

▶

$\frac{5}{5}$ is greater than $\frac{4}{4}$. Because the number is Biger.

5 ~~biger~~ is biger than 4.

# UNIT 6

## Unit 6
## Spaces
### Assessment Overview

### Before the Unit

Several types of assessment are available as you work with your class during this unit:
- Classroom Observations
- Interview Assessments (pages 56, 58, 60)
- Math Journal (Guidebook, pages 181, 189, 196)
- Written Assessment (pages 62–63)
- Self-Assessment (Guidebook, page 198)
- Portfolio Reviews (pages 57, 59, 61)

The goal is for students to move toward an understanding of the Key Mathematical Ideas and to focus on the Communication Characteristics and Learning Dispositions listed below. Observations, interviews, portfolio materials, and students' self-assessments should all contribute to your overall impression of each student's understanding. It is important to use multiple sources of information to obtain valid inferences of each student's learning over time.

## Use these guidelines as you observe students' work throughout the unit:

| Key Mathematical Ideas | Communication Characteristics | Learning Dispositions |
|---|---|---|
| ★ Perimeter can be determined by counting the units around the outside edge of a shape or surface.<br><br>★ Area can be determined by counting square units of a two-dimensional shape.<br><br>★ Shapes with the same perimeter can have different areas.<br><br>★ Shapes with the same area can have different perimeters. | ★ Did the student develop an organized approach to finding possible solutions to problems?<br><br>★ Did the student's writings about area and perimeter of various shapes make sense and indicate clear understanding? | ★ Was the student enthusiastic about the explorations?<br><br>★ Did the student show curiosity about the possible solutions?<br><br>★ Did the student show initiative in finding ways to approach problems and perseverance in looking for complete solutions? |

You can use this generalized rubric as a suggested ▶ guide as you look at students' work and listen to their responses. You may wish to adapt this rubric to make it more task-specific. Share your rubric with your class so that they can take responsibility for monitoring their own learning.

**Response Levels**

3 Accomplishes the purposes of the question, task, or unit. Mathematical communication is clear.

2 Partially accomplishes the purposes of the question, task, or unit. Mathematical communication is somewhat limited.

1 Shows fragmented understanding. Mathematical communication is vague.

## After the Unit

Once the class has completed work on this unit, pull together the various pieces listed below and make an overall evaluation of each student's performance. Record your summary on a copy of the Unit Evaluation recording sheet on page 111. You can use the completed Unit Evaluation sheet and the student's portfolio to give family members a picture of their child's progress.

 **Written Assessment**

Spaces Written Assessment, pages 62–63

 **Interview Assessment**

Week 1 • Geoboard Spaces Interview
page 56

Week 2 • Building Fences Interview
page 58

Week 3 • Silhouettes Interview
page 60

 **Portfolio Review**

Week 1 • Shapes and Areas dot-paper recordings
page 57 • Shapes That Have the Same Area posters
 • Writings About Area and Perimeter

Week 2 • Hunt for Perimeters recordings
page 59 • Fence Designs
 • Writings About Fence Designs

Week 3 • Mystery Silhouette strategies
page 61 • Squaring a Classmate plans

Note: In addition to the Portfolio Review work listed here, Home Work and Side Trip work may also have been included in the students' portfolios. See In the Portfolio, Guidebook, page 198.

 **Observation**    **Math Journal**    **Self-Assessment**

Use any notes you made while observing students work, the students' Math Journal entries, and their written Self-Assessment pieces as further insights into their mathematical thinking.

**Response Levels**

**3** Accomplishes the purposes of the question, task, or unit. Mathematical communication is clear.

**2** Partially accomplishes the purposes of the question, task, or unit. Mathematical communication is somewhat limited.

**1** Shows fragmented understanding. Mathematical communication is vague.

## About the Interview Assessment Task

During the week, show a shape on the geoboard to individual students and say, *Tell me how you would figure out the area of this shape.*

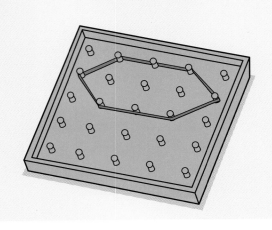

## Possible Responses

It has 4 whole squares and 4 half squares. Its area is 6 all together.

*Accurately counts the squares and partial squares within the shape. (Level 3)*

The area is 1, 2, 3, 4, 5, 6, 7, 8. You count the spaces to find the area.

*Shows some understanding of area, but counting method is not accurate. Counts half squares as whole squares. (Level 2)*

You count the whole spaces to figure out the area. This area is 4.

*Shows some understanding of area, but only counts the whole squares. (Level 2)*

The area is 11. There are 11 pegs.

*Does not show understanding of area. Counts the pegs on the geoboard to determine the area. (Level 1)*

**Response Levels**

**3** Accomplishes the purposes of the
question, task, or unit. Mathematical
communication is clear.

**2** Partially accomplishes the purposes of
the question, task, or unit. Mathematical
communication is somewhat limited.

**1** Shows fragmented understanding.
Mathematical communication is vague.

# Week 1
# Geoboard Spaces
## Portfolio Review

## Portfolio Review

At the end of this week review each student's work using the
guidelines below. Record your findings on a copy of the
Performance Observations recording sheet on page 110.

### What to look for in the students' work:

- Was the student able to make a variety of shapes on the geoboard and determine the area of each shape?

- Was the student able to make a variety of shapes on the geoboard with specific areas? Did the student try to find all of the possible shapes for a given area?

- Was the student able to determine the perimeters of shapes on the geoboard?

- Does the student show an understanding of the distinction between area and perimeter?

**In the Portfolio:**
- Shapes and Areas dot-paper recordings
- Shapes That Have the Same Area posters
- Writings About Area and Perimeter

> We have found a lot of areas and perimeters. Some numbers like 16 have only one shape, and some have a lot of shapes. We have learned a lot of shapes with the numbers from 1 to 16. I like working with areas and perimeters.

## What You Might See

▶ Makes several shapes and accurately determines each shape's area and perimeter. Tries to find all of the possible shapes for a given area. Accurately records perimeters of shapes. Shows understanding of the distinction between area and perimeter. (Level 3)

▶ Makes several shapes on the geoboard. Is sometimes accurate in determining areas and perimeters. When making shapes with the same area, does not try hard to look for all of the ways and includes a few repeats. Sometimes confuses area and perimeter. (Level 2)

▶ Makes some shapes on the geoboard, but is usually unable to determine area and perimeter. Does not focus on looking for shapes with a specific area. Often confuses area and perimeter. (Level 1)

**Response Levels**

**3** Accomplishes the purposes of the question, task, or unit. Mathematical communication is clear.

**2** Partially accomplishes the purposes of the question, task, or unit. Mathematical communication is somewhat limited.

**1** Shows fragmented understanding. Mathematical communication is vague.

## About the Interview Assessment Task

As students work this week, ask individual students, *What do you think area and perimeter mean?*

## Possible Responses

Area is the space inside a shape. Perimeter is the length of the outside edge of a shape.

*Shows understanding of the concepts of area and perimeter in general. (Level 3)*

Area is when you count boxes in a shape and perimeter is when you count around a shape.

*Shows an understanding of the meaning of area and perimeter, but does not articulate it fully. (Level 2)*

They tell how big a shape is. I keep forgetting which one is which.

*Understands that area and perimeter are measures of size, but tends to confuse the two. (Level 2)*

They tell about shapes on geoboards. I'm not sure what they mean.

*Does not show understanding of the meaning of area and perimeter. (Level 1)*

## Portfolio Review

 At the end of this week review each student's work using the guidelines below. Record your findings on a copy of the Performance Observations recording sheet on page 110.

### What to look for in the students' work:

- **Was the student able to find things around the room with specific perimeters, then measure and record them?**

- **Was the student able to design a variety of fenced enclosures, including some with large, medium, and small areas?**

- **Do the student's writings show an understanding of what kinds of shapes with a given perimeter tend to have large, medium, and small areas?**

**In the Portfolio:**
- Hunt for Perimeters recording
- Fence Designs
- Writings About Fence Designs

> I have learned that if I Imagine I was a farmer I had 40 8. Meter's of fence. I needed to make a large area for my animals. The smallest area I found was a skinny shape I couldent use that too. The Mudium size one was a traingle our a oule that fat but I dident need that either. Finely I found the largest shape it was a round fat arcle. so I made a round circle made out of fence now my animals have more room to all my animals to run and have fun. I picked a circle becuse if you picked a skinny shape it would, like only be two units in each row. so a round circle would have alot of space to run becuse its a big shape so its better.

### What You Might See

▶ Finds things around the room with specific perimeters; measures and records them. Designs a variety of enclosures with large, medium, and small areas. Writing includes generalizations regarding which shapes with a given perimeter have large, medium, and small areas. (Level 3)

▶ Finds few things around the room with specific perimeters. Fence designs indicate some effort to find shapes with large and small areas, but student does not explore thoroughly. Writing describes relative areas of specific shapes but does not include general conclusions. (Level 2)

▶ Has some difficulty finding things around the room with specific perimeters. Makes a few fence designs and does not try to find shapes with various areas. Writing shows little understanding of task. (Level 1)

**Week 3**
**Silhouettes**
**Interview Assessment**

## About the Interview Assessment Task

Approach a pair of students as they are working this week. Show one student a silhouette with an irregular shape. Ask, *What do you think the area and perimeter of this shape are, approximately, in centimeters?*

## Possible Responses

It's about the same size as the chalkboard eraser I measured. That had a perimeter of 42 cm and an area of 90 cm².

*Uses a familiar reference point on which to base an estimate. (Level 3)*

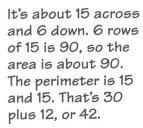

It's about 15 across and 6 down. 6 rows of 15 is 90, so the area is about 90. The perimeter is 15 and 15. That's 30 plus 12, or 42.

*Estimates centimeters by using width of fingers, an efficient and accurate counting method. Makes a reasonable estimate. (Level 3)*

It's about 15 across and 6 down. The area is 6 rows of 15, or about 90. The perimeter is 15 plus 15 plus 6 plus 6. That's 42.

*Uses a centimeter ruler to find the length and width of the shape, then estimates its area and perimeter. (Level 3)*

It's 15 across and 6 down so the perimeter is 21 centimeters.

*Makes an error in finding the perimeter. Is unwilling to estimate the area without outlining the object and counting the squares. (Level 2)*

## Portfolio Review

 At the end of this week review each student's work using the guidelines below. Record your findings on a copy of the Performance Observations recording sheet on page 110.

**In the Portfolio:**
- Mystery Silhouette strategies
- Squaring a Classmate plans

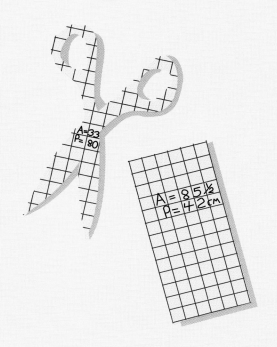

### What to look for in the students' work:

- Was the student able to find areas and perimeters of several items around the room?

- Was the student able to use measurement skills and logical thinking to match silhouettes with their measurements?

- Do the student's plans for "squaring a classmate" show an understanding of the concepts of and distinctions between area and perimeter?

## What You Might See

▶ Determines the area and perimeter of several items and uses logical thinking to match silhouettes to their measurements accurately. Plans clearly show understanding of the concepts of and distinctions between area and perimeter. (Level 3)

▶ Determines the area and perimeter of several items. Is able to match most silhouettes with their measurements, but does not include a description of strategies in the recording. Distinctions between concepts of area and perimeter are not entirely clear in writing. (Level 2)

▶ Has some difficulty determining the area and perimeter of items around the room. Matches a few silhouettes with their measurements, but does not write about strategies. Still shows some confusion between concepts of area and perimeter. (Level 1)

# UNIT 6

## Unit 6
## Spaces
### Written Assessment

## About the Written Assessment Task

This assessment gives you an opportunity to see students' written responses to a particular question related to the unit. It is not an evaluation of the entire unit. Use this task anytime during the unit or as a pre-unit assessment. You may also use this task with just a few students when you need extra insight into their mathematical thinking.

This assessment task focuses on the students' understanding of area and perimeter and the ability to communicate ideas clearly.

**Materials:** Each student will need a full sheet of paper.

**Assessment Task:** Ask the students to write in response to the following: ***Imagine that you have a pet rabbit and you are going to make a rectangular pen for it that is 4 feet long and 3 feet wide. Tell how you would figure out how much fencing you would need to buy.***

## Possible Responses

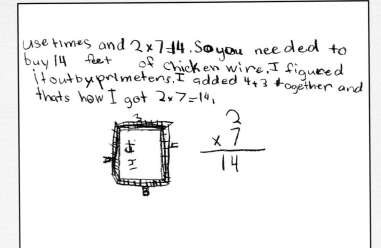

◄ Student's plan shows understanding of concept of perimeter. Student uses a combination of addition and multiplication to find the total amount of fencing needed. (Level 3)

My answer is 14

$7 \times 2 = 14$

$2 \times 7 = 14$

$14 \div 7 = 2$

$14 \div 2 = 7$

◀ More discussion with student is
necessary. Student gives correct
answer, but does not explain solution
method. (Level 2)

Student does not write about a
realistic plan or show correct answer.
(Level 1)  ▶

## Before the Unit

Several types of assessment are available as you work with your class during this unit:

- Classroom Observations
- Interview Assessments (pages 66, 68, 70, 72, 74)
- Math Journal (Guidebook, pages 213, 221, 229, 244)
- Written Assessment (pages 76–77)
- Self-Assessment (Guidebook, page 246)
- Portfolio Reviews (pages 67, 69, 71, 73, 75)

The goal is for students to move toward an understanding of the Key Mathematical Ideas and to focus on the Communication Characteristics and Learning Dispositions listed below. Observations, interviews, portfolio materials, and students' self-assessments should all contribute to your overall impression of each student's understanding. It is important to use multiple sources of information to obtain valid inferences of each student's learning over time.

## Use these guidelines as you observe students' work throughout the unit:

| Key Mathematical Ideas | Communication Characteristics | Learning Dispositions |
|---|---|---|
| ★ There are patterns and relationships among numbers and in the structure of our place-value system. | ★ How clear and complete were the student's recordings and descriptions of her work? | ★ Did the student show perseverance and concentration when working on the tasks in this unit? |
| ★ The ability to create a model and determine when a model would be useful increases math power. | | ★ Was the student flexible, showing an ability to look at numbers in new ways and to change an approach to a problem when it wasn't working? |
| ★ Every whole-number multiplication problem, and the partial products within it, can be perceived as a rectangle. | | |
| ★ Estimation is an important mathematical tool. | | |

You can use this generalized rubric as a suggested guide as you look at students' work and listen to their responses. You may wish to adapt this rubric to make it more task-specific. Share your rubric with your class so that they can take responsibility for monitoring their own learning.

### Response Levels

3 Accomplishes the purposes of the question, task, or unit. Mathematical communication is clear.

2 Partially accomplishes the purposes of the question, task, or unit. Mathematical communication is somewhat limited.

1 Shows fragmented understanding. Mathematical communication is vague.

## After the Unit

Once the class has completed work on this unit, pull together the various pieces listed below and make an overall evaluation of each student's performance. Record your summary on a copy of the Unit Evaluation recording sheet on page 111. You can use the completed Unit Evaluation sheet and the student's portfolio to give family members a picture of their child's progress.

 **Written Assessment**

Representations Written Assessment, pages 76–77

 **Interview Assessment**

Week 1 • Squares and Cubes Interview
page 66

Week 2 • Under Construction... Interview
page 68

Week 3 • Rectangles Inside Rectangles
page 70    Interview

Week 4 • Theater Works Interview
page 72

Week 5 • Full of Beans Interview
page 74

 **Portfolio Review**

Week 1 • Squares and Cubes reports
page 67

Week 2 • Weekly Observations
page 69

Week 3 • Rectangle Posters
page 71 • Writing About Division

Week 4 • Theater Profits recordings
page 73 • Letter to the Theater Manager

Week 5 • How Many People Fit in Our Room?
page 75    plan
         • Jar Estimation plans and reports
         • Balloon Estimation plan

Note: In addition to the Portfolio Review work listed here, Home Work and Side Trip work may also have been included in the children's portfolios. See In the Portfolio, Guidebook, page 246.

 **Observation**     **Math Journal**     **Self-Assessment**

Use any notes you made while observing students work, the students' Math Journal entries, and their written Self-Assessment pieces as further insights into their mathematical thinking.

# UNIT 7

## Week 1
## Squares and Cubes
### Interview Assessment

## About the Interview Assessment Task

As students work during Along the Way, ask individual students, **Have you tried 16 yet? Can it be a square? a cube?**

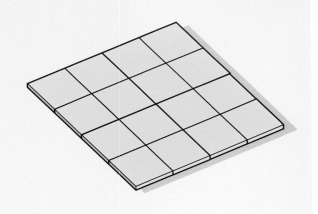

## Possible Responses

We figured out that if a number is the answer to a problem like 2 x 2 or 3 x 3 or 4 x 4, it can be a square. Sixteen is 4 times 4, so it's a square. I'll see if it can be a cube. No, it can't.

*Demonstrates knowledge of both concepts. Finds and uses patterns in the sequence. (Level 3)*

Well, I can make a square all right, but I don't know about a cube. Here's a cube!

*Correctly arranges 16 into a square, but makes a 2 x 2 x 4 solid and calls it a cube. (Level 2)*

I can make a square from 16 chips. We just found out 8 is a cube, so maybe 16 is just two of those put together.

*Demonstrates knowledge of one of the two concepts. Tries to use patterns as a strategy, but makes an incorrect assumption. (Level 2)*

I couldn't get it into a square or a cube.

*Either does not understand how to build squares or cubes, or does not persist in trying to build them for the number. (Level 1)*

## Portfolio Review

 At the end of this week review each student's work using the guidelines below. Record your findings on a copy of the Performance Observations recording sheet on page 110.

**In the Portfolio:**
- Squares and Cubes report

### What to look for in the students' work:

- Was the student able to identify and model the square and cube numbers from 1 to 100?

- Was the student able to make grid-paper representations of his squares and cubes?

- Does the student's recording show her work and tell her conclusions?

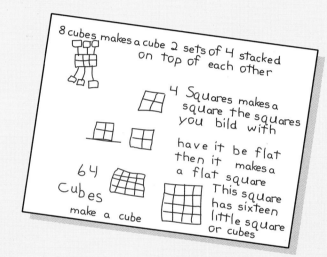

## What You Might See

▶ Grasps ideas of square and cube and identifies numbers from 1 to 100 that are examples of each. Makes an organized recording of week's work. Grid-paper representations of squares and cubes are all present and accurate. (Level 3)

▶ Initially struggles to find square and cube numbers. Identifies most of the squares and cubes but sometimes confuses the terms. Grid-paper models, in combination with recording, provide clear record of work. (Level 2)

▶ Is unable to identify either square or cube numbers. Becomes distracted by building squares and cubes, and neglects to attend to number. Does not produce a recording, but produces some paper models that come close to matching the models made with blocks. (Level 1)

## About the Interview Assessment Task

During the week, show individual students a Base Ten Block model of the number 1437. Ask, ***What number do these blocks model? Can you read it to me?***

## Possible Responses

It's one thousand four hundred and thirty-seven.

*Identifies the number with ease. (Level 3)*

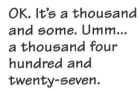

OK. It's a thousand and some. Umm... a thousand four hundred and twenty-seven.

*Understands how to interpret the model, but makes a counting error. (Level 2)*

Let's see. This is a thousand. Here's four hundred. And this is thirty-seven.

*Interprets the model piece by piece, but doesn't interpret it as a whole. (Level 2)*

I'm not sure how to say it. There are seven of this kind and three of this kind....

*Even when questioned further, does not appear to understand what the base ten models represent. (Level 1)*

## Portfolio Review

 Since there is no work for the portfolio this week, your observations of students will be especially important.

**In the Portfolio:**
- Weekly Observations

### What to look for in the students' work:

- Was the student able to build models of numbers with the Base Ten Blocks?

- Was the student able to communicate clearly about the numbers he was building and the base-ten system in general?

- Was the student able to work effectively with her group members?

## Sample Observations

▶ Builds accurate representations of numbers with Base Ten Blocks. Communicates an understanding of and confidence with the base-ten system. (Level 3)

▶ Is frustrated by the group's dynamics, so puts little effort into the task. Indicates a fair level of understanding about the base-ten system in conversations with group members and with teacher individually. (Level 2)

▶ Is unclear about how to model numbers with Base Ten Blocks. Often confuses hundreds and thousands. Is reluctant to participate in group discussions. When interviewed individually, expresses frustration with the modeling task. (Level 1)

**Response Levels**

**3** Accomplishes the purposes of the question, task, or unit. Mathematical communication is clear.

**2** Partially accomplishes the purposes of the question, task, or unit. Mathematical communication is somewhat limited.

**1** Shows fragmented understanding. Mathematical communication is vague.

## About the Interview Assessment Task

During Along the Way, say to individual students, ***Tell me about the rectangles you've made for your multiplication problem.***

## Possible Responses

We're showing 15 x 14. We made the rectangle for 150. Now we're doing the 60 rectangle. 15 times 14 is like 15 times 10 and 15 times 4.

*Clearly explains how the block rectangles relate to a solution to the multiplication problem. (Level 3)*

See, there are three rectangles inside our 15 times 14 rectangle. One shows 15 times 10. These two both show two 15s, or 30. If you add the small rectangles up, it's the same as the answer to 15 x 14.

*Clearly explains the relationship between the partial-product rectangles and the product rectangle. (Level 3)*

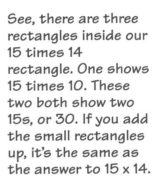

The answer is 210, because it's like ten times 15, and then 4 times 15.

*Response demonstrates correct mental arithmetic, but does not explain the relevance of the rectangles. (Level 2)*

We made a big rectangle and now we're cutting it into smaller shapes.

*Does not focus on relating the blocks to the day's problem. (Level 1)*

**Week 3**
**Rectangles Inside Rectangles**
Portfolio Review

## Portfolio Review

At the end of this week review each student's work using the guidelines below. Record your findings on a copy of the Performance Observations recording sheet on page 110.

**What to look for in the students' work:**

- Was the student able to build product rectangles for multiplication problems and the partial-product rectangles within them?

- Was the student able to cut out grid-paper models of partial-product rectangles and make a poster showing how they join to form the product rectangle?

- Did the student label the rectangles on the poster to clarify?

- Does the student's writing about a division problem show an understanding of the relationship between multiplication and division and the understanding that blocks can represent both?

**In the Portfolio:**
- Rectangle Poster
- Writing About Division

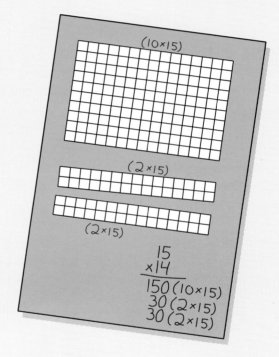

## What You Might See

▶ Models product rectangles and identifies the partial-product rectangles within them. Posters clearly reflect work with blocks and are well-labeled and organized. Looking Back writing indicates understanding of a relationship between multiplication and division and how rectangles can represent them. (Level 3)

▶ Easily models product rectangles. Struggles at first to locate the partial-product rectangles. Posters show a progression toward an understanding of partial products as rectangles. Looking Back writing shows some confusion about the relationship between multiplication and division. (Level 2)

▶ Work is often unfocused. Often needs assistance to model product rectangles with Base Ten Blocks. Is unable to extend the work to partial-product rectangles. Posters do not show solutions, but do show an effort to understand the idea of multiplication as a rectangle. (Level 1)

**Response Levels**

**3** Accomplishes the purposes of the question, task, or unit. Mathematical communication is clear.

**2** Partially accomplishes the purposes of the question, task, or unit. Mathematical communication is somewhat limited.

**1** Shows fragmented understanding. Mathematical communication is vague.

## About the Interview Assessment Task

During the week, ask individual students, *What if the theater held 13 rows of 13 chairs? How many seats would there be all together? Tell me how you know.*

## Possible Responses

Let's see. 13 times 13. That would be a hundred and thirty, plus 3 more 13s, that's 3, 6, 9, 39. 130 plus 39 is 169.

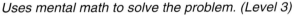

*Uses mental math to solve the problem. (Level 3)*

Hmm... I'll line up 13 rows of 13. That's 10, 20, 30...150, 160, 161, 162... 168, 169.

*Models the problem with blocks, and counts by tens and ones to determine the total. (Level 3)*

Here are 13 rows of 13. That's 10, 20, 30...150, 160, 170, 171,...178, 179.

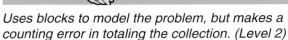

*Uses blocks to model the problem, but makes a counting error in totaling the collection. (Level 2)*

There are 144 seats in the theater.

*Refers to previous problem information. Does not realize how new seating information affects the total. (Level 1)*

## Portfolio Review

At the end of this week review each student's work using the guidelines below. Record your findings on a copy of the Performance Observations recording sheet on page 110.

**In the Portfolio:**
- Theater Profits recording
- Letter to the Theater Manager

**What to look for in the students' work:**

- Was the student able to think through the problem and keep notes about the various phases of the work?

- Was the student able to decide which variable(s) to change in response to a particular outcome?

- Did the student's letter to the theater manager clearly present figures and reasoning?

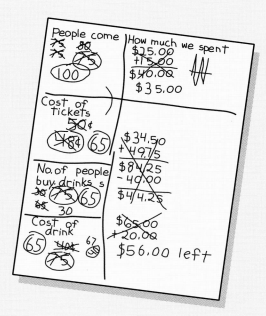

## What You Might See

▶ Keeps the various problem elements in mind throughout the work and is able to see the relationship between a change in one or two variables and the end result. Accurately reflects each phase of the problem-solving process in the work notes, and writes a clear letter to the manager. (Level 3)

▶ Keeps in mind most elements. Sometimes loses track of what needs to be calculated next, but seeks help and gets back on track. Includes many, but not all, of the solution steps in the work notes. Presents most of the relevant figures in the letter to the theater manager. (Level 2)

▶ Is unable to grasp the idea that a change in one number in the problem can affect the solution. Has difficulty staying on task, and relies on partner to move the work along. Cannot interpret the notes when asked. Letter is unrelated to the mathematics of the problem. (Level 1)

## About the Interview Assessment Task

During the week, show individual students a page in a dictionary or encyclopedia. Ask, *About how many letters do you think are on this page? How would you go about making a good estimate?*

## Possible Responses

I'd make a square outline and see about how many letters would fit in it. Then I'd see how many squares would fit on the whole page and multiply it.

*Uses visual thinking and operations, and clearly describes a logical process. (Level 3)*

I'd count the letters in this line, count how many lines on the page, and multiply. I think I'd need a calculator, though.

*Uses counting and operations, and clearly describes a logical process. (Level 3)*

I'd use a ruler to measure how many letters are in an inch—15. Then I'd measure the page. It's 8 inches across and 10 inches down. So that's 80 inches times 15.

*Describes a logical process, but includes a flaw in the method. (Level 2)*

I'd say it's about 300 letters. It just looks like about that many.

*Makes a guess without attempting to use counting or visual strategies. (Level 1)*

## Portfolio Review

At the end of this week review each child's work using the guidelines below. Record your findings on a copy of the Performance Observations recording sheet on page 110.

**In the Portfolio:**
- How Many People Fit in Our Room? plan
- Jar Estimation plans and reports
- Balloon Estimation plan

### What to look for in the students' work:

- Was the student able to imagine ways to use physical tools to aid in the estimation of large quantities?

- Were the student's written explanations of estimation plans clear and logical?

- After testing each plan, was the student able to write a report to summarize the findings and give a resulting estimate?

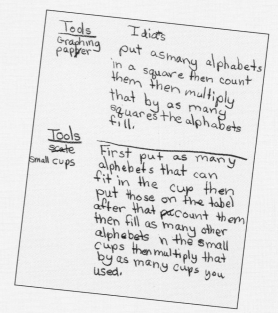

Tools
Graphing
papper

I did's
put asmany alphabets in a square then count them then multiply that by as many squares the alphabets fill.

Tools
scale
Small cups

First put as many alphebets that can fit in the cup then put those on the tabel after that pa count them then fill as many other alphebets n the small cups then multiply that by as many cups you used.

## What You Might See

▶ Thinks of logical and inventive strategies for the use of various estimation tools. Accurately describes each strategy in writing. Each plan is executed carefully and completely and results in reasonable estimates. (Level 3)

▶ Written descriptions of plans are not always complete. Execution of each plan is done fairly accurately, and the written report gives a resulting estimate. Does not otherwise detail findings or conclusions. (Level 2)

▶ Makes one estimation plan for one or two problems, but writes vague descriptions. When trying to execute the plan, gets sidetracked onto a counting method, and later becomes frustrated and produces a random estimate unrelated to the estimation strategies attempted. Written report consists only of this random estimate. (Level 1)

# UNIT 7

## Unit 7
## Representations
### Written Assessment

## About the Written Assessment Task

This assessment gives you an opportunity to see students' written response to a particular question related to the unit. Use this task anytime during the unit or as a pre-unit assessment. You may also use this task with just a few students when you need extra insight into their mathematical thinking.

This assessment task focuses on the students' understanding of multiplication.

**Materials:** Each student will need a full sheet of paper.

**Assessment Task:** On the chalkboard, write the problem $14 \times 15$ in vertical notation. *When someone asks you to solve this problem in your head, what do you think about? Tell how you go about solving the problem. If you wish, use drawings to help you explain.*

## Possible Responses

How I am going to solve that problem is make the 14 to 10. After, I would multiply 10 times 15. Then, the answer that I got I would mutiply 4 times 15. Finally what I got for 4 times 15 I add to what 10 times 15 is. That might be a way to do that problem. P.s. I made 4 x15 because 14 has a four in the ones.

15
x14 — make it 10
answer) 150
answer 4 x15 = 60
then
add 210

◄ Student uses numbers and sentences to explain the process clearly. Has a good understanding of what multiplication is. (Level 3)

15
×14

① First I would moltiplie 15 ×4 wihich equals 60,

② Next I would put the 60 under the 15 ×14 like So 15 ×10 / 60,

③ Third I would moltiplie 15 ×10 which = 150

④ forth I would 15 under the 15 ×64 / 60 / 15

⑤ last I would add 60 +15 whichu = 75,

◀ Student gives steps involved in solving the problem, but makes an error in computation. Does not notice that the resulting number is obviously too low. (Level 2)

Student appears to be unable to work the problem. Does not explain thinking. (Level 1) ▶

your you can do 15×14 and then you got your awser.

# Unit 8
# Shaping Relationships
## Assessment Overview

## Before the Unit

Several types of assessment are available as you work with your class during this unit:

- Classroom Observations
- Interview Assessments (pages 80, 82, 84)
- Math Journal (Guidebook, pages 265, 269)
- Written Assessment (pages 86–87)
- Self-Assessment (Guidebook, page 278)
- Portfolio Reviews (pages 81, 83, 85)

The goal is for students to move toward an understanding of the Key Mathematical Ideas and to focus on the Communication Characteristics and Learning Dispositions listed below. Observations, interviews, portfolio materials, and students' self-assessments should all contribute to your overall impression of each student's understanding. It is important to use multiple sources of information to obtain valid inferences of each student's learning over time.

## Use these guidelines as you observe students' work throughout the unit:

| Key Mathematical Ideas | Communication Characteristics | Learning Dispositions |
|---|---|---|
| ★ Every shape is made up of other shapes. <br><br> ★ Shapes can be classified in many ways, and groups of shapes are related to each other in many ways. <br><br> ★ Special geometric terms are helpful for communicating clearly about shapes. | ★ How clear and organized were the student's descriptions and recordings? <br><br> ★ Did the student's descriptions make sense to other students in the class? <br><br> ★ Was the student able to find many ways to group the Polygon Tiles? | ★ Did the student show flexibility of thinking? <br><br> ★ Did the student show perseverance in solving puzzles and looking for patterns? <br><br> ★ Did the student show curiosity and enthusiasm for the tasks? |

You can use this generalized rubric as a suggested guide as you look at students' work and listen to their responses. You may wish to adapt this rubric to make it more task-specific. Share your rubric with your class so that they can take responsibility for monitoring their own learning. ▶

**Response Levels**

3 Accomplishes the purposes of the question, task, or unit. Mathematical communication is clear.

2 Partially accomplishes the purposes of the question, task, or unit. Mathematical communication is somewhat limited.

1 Shows fragmented understanding. Mathematical communication is vague.

## After the Unit

Once the class has completed work on this unit, pull together the various pieces listed below and make an overall evaluation of each student's performance. Record your summary on a copy of the Unit Evaluation recording sheet on page 111. You can use the completed Unit Evaluation sheet and the student's portfolio to give family members a picture of their child's progress.

 **Written Assessment**

Shaping Relationships Written Assessment, pages 86–87

 **Interview Assessment**

Week 1 • Shapes in Shapes Interview
page 80

Week 2 • Geometry Dictionaries Interview
page 82

Week 3 • A Mathematician's Challenge
page 84     Interview

 **Portfolio Review**

Week 1 • Cut and Tell recordings
page 81 • Tangram Puzzles
        • Guess My Shape Puzzles

Week 2 • Geometry Dictionaries
page 83

Week 3 • Written summary of the week
page 85

Note: In addition to the Portfolio Review work listed here, Home Work and Side Trip work may also have been included in the students' portfolios. See In the Portfolio, Guidebook, page 278.

 **Observation**     **Math Journal**     **Self-Assessment**

Use any notes you made while observing students work, the students' Math Journal entries, and their written Self-Assessment pieces as further insights into their mathematical thinking.

## About the Interview Assessment Task

As the students work this week, show Geoblock shape O to individual students and say, **_Tell me some things you notice about this block._**

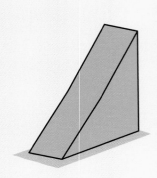

## Possible Responses:

It has two triangles and three rectangles. Those edges are the shortest. This is a right angle. It looks like a slide.

_Focuses on several attributes of the block. Descriptions are clear and mathematical language is used properly. (Level 3)_

These two edges are equal. This side is a triangle. This side is a rectangle. This is a square angle. This is a pointy angle.

_Focuses on several attributes of the block. Descriptions are correct and understandable, although mathematical language may be informal. (Level 3)_

There's a triangle. There's a rectangle.

_Focuses on one attribute (in this case shape of the face). Descriptions correct and understandable. (Level 2)_

It's a block.

_Even when asked to elaborate, does not show understanding of attributes or components of the shape. (Level 1)_

## Portfolio Review

At the end of this week review each student's work using the guidelines below. Record your findings on a copy of the Performance Observations recording sheet on page 110.

What to look for
in the students' work:

• Are Cut and Tell Recordings present? Do they include predictions as well as cut rectangles?

• Are there at least two tangram puzzles, one that can be solved and one that cannot?

• Do the Guess My Shape puzzles show attention to attributes of shapes, and are clues clear enough that the puzzles can be solved?

**In the Portfolio:**
• Cut and Tell recordings
• Tangram Puzzles
• Guess My Shape Puzzles

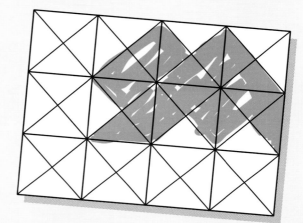

### What You Might See

▶ Work is present and complete, and indicates that the student understood the important aspects of the Day Trips. Guess My Shape puzzles include mention of a variety of attributes, and clues are clear enough that puzzles can be solved. (Level 3)

▶ Most work is present and complete. Clues on Guess My Shape puzzles are not clear enough for the puzzles to be solved. (Level 2)

▶ Some work is missing or incomplete. It is difficult to interpret the student's ideas from the recordings. When the student is asked, responses suggest very limited understanding of the important aspects of the work. (Level 1)

## About the Interview Assessment Task

During Along the Way, show two Polygon Tiles to individual students and say, *Tell me how these shapes are alike and how they are different.*

## Possible Responses

Both have a square corner and straight sides and are flat. They're different because this one has three sides and the other has four. These angles are different than these angles.

*Tells many ways in which the figures are alike and different. Uses some appropriate mathematical language, although may not use all terms available. (Level 3)*

These corners are alike. This is a triangle and this has four sides.

*Offers a few similarities and differences, noticing more than one attribute. Uses some appropriate mathematical language. (Level 2)*

This is a triangle and this has more sides.

*Offers only one or two similarities or differences, based on one attribute. Even when asked, cannot expand list. (Level 1)*

This has three sides and it's pointy.

*Describes a shape in isolation. Even when asked, does not relate two shapes to each other. (Level 1)*

## Portfolio Review

 At the end of this week review each student's work using the guidelines below. Record your findings on a copy of the Performance Observations recording sheet on page 110.

**In the Portfolio:**
• Geometry Dictionaries

**What to look for in the students' work:**

• Does the student make a few different dictionary pages showing groups of shapes?

• Does the student group shapes according to more than one attribute?

• Do the dictionary pages include tracings of shapes, definitions, nicknames, and mathematical terms?

• Does the student clearly communicate ideas about attributes of shapes?

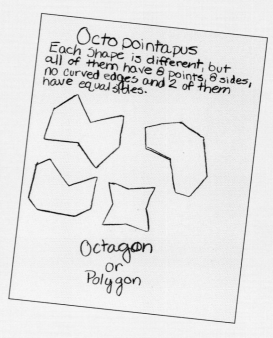

## What You Might See

▶ Student makes many pages for a variety of polygons. Several of the shape groups indicate student's attention to more than one attribute at a time. The scheme for grouping changes from page to page. Dictionary pages are complete and communicate the definitions of the shapes clearly. (Level 3)

▶ Student makes several pages for a variety of polygons. Some shape groups show student's attention to more than one attribute. Schemes for grouping are limited to one or two attributes. Dictionary pages are mostly complete, but communication of definitions could use clarification. (Level 2)

▶ Student makes few pages for a limited number of polygons. Most shape groups indicate student's attention to only one attribute. Definitions are missing or poorly communicated. Student cannot add verbally to what is on the pages. (Level 1)

## About the Interview Assessment Task

As the students work, show Geoblock shape *N* to individual students and say, ***Tell me how many vertices, edges, and faces this polyhedron has.***

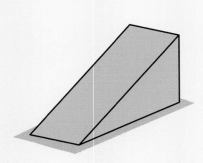

## Possible Responses

It has six vertices, nine edges, and five faces.

*Uses terminology properly and counts correctly. (Level 3)*

It has six vertices, eight edges, and five faces.

*Uses terminology properly, but makes an error in counting. (Level 2)*

It has six, nine, and five.

*Counts correctly, but even when asked, cannot come up with all three names for the parts of the polyhedron. (Level 2)*

Five, ten, and five.

*Counts incorrectly. Even when asked, cannot come up with all three names for the parts of the polyhedron. (Level 1)*

## Portfolio Review

At the end of this week review each student's work using the guidelines below. Record your findings on a copy of the Performance Observations recording sheet on page 110.

**In the Portfolio:**
- Written summary of the week

### What to look for in the students' work:

- Does the student's recording indicate an attempt to understand the components of shapes?

- Does the student use precise terminology?

- Is the student able to communicate ideas clearly?

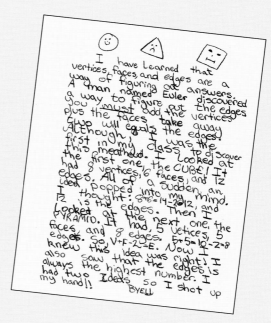

### What You Might See

▶ Student tells about the week's experiences clearly and in an organized way and discusses components of shapes, correctly using the terms *vertex, edge,* and *face*. (Level 3)

▶ Student tells about his learnings and experiences. Writing lacks some clarity and completeness. Occasionally misuses terminology. (Level 2)

▶ Recording lacks clarity and completeness. Student is unable to expand significantly on the writing or clarify it, even when asked to do so orally. (Level 1)

**Unit 8**
**Shaping Relationships**
Written Assessment

**Response Levels**

3  Accomplishes the purposes of the
   question, task, or unit. Mathematical
   communication is clear.

2  Partially accomplishes the purposes of
   the question, task, or unit. Mathematical
   communication is somewhat limited.

1  Shows fragmented understanding.
   Mathematical communication is vague.

## About the Written Assessment Task

This assessment gives you an opportunity to
see students' written response to a particular
question related to the unit. It is not an
evaluation of the entire unit. Use this task
anytime during the unit or as a pre-unit
assessment. You may also use this task with
just a few students when you need extra
insight into their mathematical thinking.

This assessment task focuses on the students'
knowledge of two-dimensional shapes and
their ability to communicate ideas about the
shapes.

**Materials:** Each student will need a full sheet
of paper.

**Assessment Task:** Tell the students, *Draw as*
*many different polygons as you can and*
*label them with their names. Use names or*
*descriptions to tell how shapes are alike and*
*how they are different.*

## Possible Responses

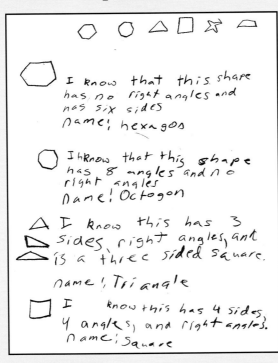

◀ Student draws several polygons. All are
labeled. (Level 3)

Triangles
△◁△ I Know that these shapes
have 3 sides and 3 points. They can
be different sides.

squares
□□□ These shape have 4 points
a 4 side. Each side has to be the
same size.

rectangle
▭▯▭ Each has 4side and 4 points
but the side are longer than
the other but the have to
be parrelt.

circle
○◯◯ Each shape has no strate
edges. The whole thing is round.

oval
⬭ Each shape looks like
a circle. They are longer than a
circle. It looks like it got
streched.

Hexagon
⬠ It has 6 sides and
6 points.

I Learned mathimatical names for
shapes

◀ Student draws and labels many
different polygons, (although
circles and ovals are not polygons).
Commentary shows a good idea of
relationships among shapes. (Level 2)

Student draws a few polygons.
Although the commentary does not
reveal much knowledge of shapes,
the student has used names to
describe the shapes. (Level 2)  ▶

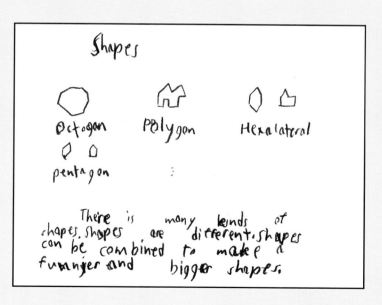

Shapes

Octogon    POlygon    Hexalateral

pentagon

There is many kinds of
shapes. shapes are different. shapes
can be combined to make a
funnyer and bigger shapes.

### Before the Unit

Several types of assessment are available as you work with your class during this unit:

- Classroom Observations
- Interview Assessments (pages 90, 92, 94, 96, 98)
- Math Journal (Guidebook, pages 288, 301, 308, 317, 325)
- Written Assessment (pages 100–101)
- Self-Assessment (Guidebook, page 326)
- Portfolio Reviews (pages 91, 93, 95, 97, 99)

The goal is for students to move toward an understanding of the Key Mathematical Ideas and to focus on the Communication Characteristics and Learning Dispositions listed below. Observations, interviews, portfolio materials, and students' self-assessments should all contribute to your overall impression of each student's understanding. It is important to use multiple sources of information to obtain valid inferences of each student's learning over time.

## Use these guidelines as you observe students' work throughout the unit:

| Key Mathematical Ideas | Communication Characteristics | Learning Dispositions |
|---|---|---|
| ★ The study of any event or situation in the world around us holds opportunities for mathematical investigations.<br><br>★ A scale drawing shows objects larger or smaller than actual size, but the ratio between the different elements and their actual size is constant.<br><br>★ In real problem-solving situations, many solution strategies can be used, combining a variety of mathematical techniques in different ways. | ★ Was the student organized in his approach to the problem-solving situations?<br><br>★ Did his writings make sense? | ★ Did the student show flexibility when approaching problems?<br><br>★ Did the student persevere even when a problem seemed difficult?<br><br>★ Did the student concentrate well on the various problems and explorations? |

You can use this generalized rubric as a suggested guide as you look at students' work and listen to their responses. You may wish to adapt this rubric to make it more task-specific. Share your rubric with your class so that they can take responsibility for monitoring their own learning. ▶

**Response Levels**

3 Accomplishes the purposes of the question, task, or unit. Mathematical communication is clear.

2 Partially accomplishes the purposes of the question, task, or unit. Mathematical communication is somewhat limited.

1 Shows fragmented understanding. Mathematical communication is vague.

### After the Unit

Once the class has completed work on this unit, pull together the various pieces listed below and make an overall evaluation of each student's performance. Record your summary on a copy of the Unit Evaluation recording sheet on page 111. You can use the completed Unit Evaluation sheet and the student's portfolio to give family members a picture of their child's progress.

 **Written Assessment**

Dinosaur Days Written Assessment, pages 100–101

 **Interview Assessment**

Week 1 • Dinosaur Database Interview
page 90

Week 2 • Life-Size Dinosaurs Interview
page 92

Week 3 • Dinosaur Drawings Interview
page 94

Week 4 • Amazing Relationships Interview
page 96

Week 5 • Supersaurus Stumpers Interview
page 98

 **Portfolio Review**

Week 1 • Dinosaur Poster
page 91 • Averaging report

Week 2 • Original Plan Diagram
page 93 • Revised Plan Diagram

Week 3 • Scale Drawings of dinosaurs
page 95 • Writing about drawing to scale

Week 4 • Comparison Clue solution
page 97 • Explanation recording
• Puzzle and Answer recording
• Object and Dimension list
• Amazing Relationships recording

Week 5 • Supersaurus Stumper recording
page 99 • Mile-Long Parade recording

Note: In addition to the Portfolio Review work listed here, Home Work and Side Trip work may also have been included in the students' portfolios. See In the Portfolio, Guidebook, page 326.

 **Observation**　 **Math Journal**　 **Self-Assessment**

Use any notes you made while observing students work, the students' Math Journal entries, and their written Self-Assessment pieces as further insights into their mathematical thinking.

**Response Levels**

**3** Accomplishes the purposes of the question, task, or unit. Mathematical communication is clear.

**2** Partially accomplishes the purposes of the question, task, or unit. Mathematical communication is somewhat limited.

**1** Shows fragmented understanding. Mathematical communication is vague.

## About the Interview Assessment Task

As students work this week, show individual students a list of the following numbers: 20, 25, 28, 31, and 34. *Find the average of these numbers. Use any method you want*. Make Rainbow Cubes, pencil and paper, and calculators available.

## Possible Responses

I just add up all the numbers. Then I divide by how many numbers there were. It's a bit more than 27.

*Uses paper and pencil or a calculator to calculate the average successfully. (Level 3)*

I make a line of cubes for each number. Then I take cubes off the taller stacks and move them to the lower until all the stacks are as even as I can get them. That's the average. It's about 27— a little more, because there are leftover cubes.

*Using cubes, applies a "smoothing out" strategy to find the average successfully. (Level 3)*

I'll count out cubes for each of your numbers and put them in a big pile. Then I'll divide them up equally to find the average. It's 23.

*Beginning of strategy is successful, but when dividing cubes up equally, disregards original number of pieces of data. (Level 2)*

Well, here are cubes to match the numbers. I don't know what comes next.

*Puts cubes out to represent each number given, but cannot progress further, even with teacher prompting. (Level 1)*

## Portfolio Review

At the end of this week review each student's work using the guidelines below. Record your findings on a copy of the Performance Observations recording sheet on page 110.

### What to look for in the students' work:

- Is the student able to describe a technique for averaging numbers?

- Does the student create a dinosaur poster showing a variety of interesting information?

- Does the student contribute to the class database, helping to average the information within cells?

**In the Portfolio:**
- Dinosaur Poster
- Averaging report

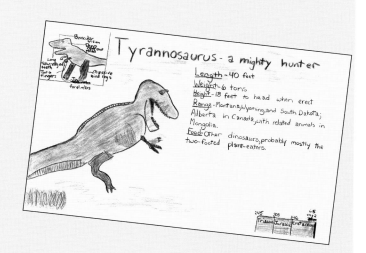

## What You Might See

▶ Shows a serious research effort in the dinosaur poster, combining information from many sources. The student's averaging report explains a technique that would work for any set of numbers. (Level 3)

▶ Has several interesting facts in the dinosaur poster, but has some incorrect information. The student's averaging report describes a process for a particular set of numbers. (Level 2)

▶ Has only one or two pieces of information in the dinosaur poster. The averaging report is incomplete or explains an unreliable process. (Level 1)

**Week 2**
**Life-Size Dinosaurs**
**Interview Assessment**

## About the Interview Assessment Task

As students work during Along the Way, point to one dinosaur on the diagram a pair is making and say, *How do you know this dinosaur fits here? How do you know the dimensions are right?*

## Possible Responses

Tyrannosaurus is 40 feet long. The playground is 160 feet wide, so half would be 80 feet. Half of that is 40, so he'd fit here. Then he's 20 feet tall.

*Correctly partitions the length and height of the playground sketch and locates the dinosaur's dimensions in relationship to the playground dimensions. (Level 3)*

The playground is 180 feet long, so we marked where every ten feet would be. We did the same with this other side. Tyrannosaurus goes here: 40 feet long and 20 feet tall.

*Used trial and error to mark off each side in 10-foot increments. Correctly positions dinosaur using these marks. (Level 3)*

The playground is 180 feet long. We can try to line up the dinosaurs on that side. First we put Tyrannosaurus, he's the longest. I think he'll come to here.

*Focuses on only one dimension to position dinosaurs. Guesses to position dinosaur's length rather than subdividing the side length. (Level 2)*

He fits there because I drew him there. I made him really scary.

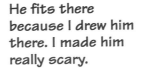

*Does not relate the size of the dinosaur to the dimensions of the playground. Draws the dinosaur much bigger (or smaller) than the scale. (Level 1)*

**Response Levels**

**3** Accomplishes the purposes of the question, task, or unit. Mathematical communication is clear.

**2** Partially accomplishes the purposes of the question, task, or unit. Mathematical communication is somewhat limited.

**1** Shows fragmented understanding. Mathematical communication is vague.

## Portfolio Review

At the end of this week review each student's work using the guidelines below. Record your findings on a copy of the Performance Observations recording sheet on page 110.

**In the Portfolio:**
- Original Plan Diagram
- Revised Plan Diagram

**What to look for in the students' work:**

- Is the student able to draw a diagram showing the approximate dimensions of the playground?

- Is the student able to use some system to subdivide these dimensions in order to position the eight dinosaurs?

- Is the student able to indicate the dimensions (height and length) of the dinosaurs on the diagram, approximately to scale?

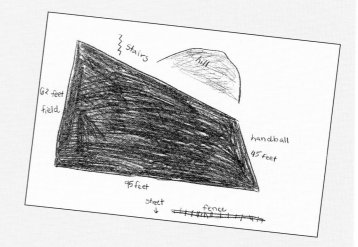

## What You Might See

▶ Diagram is a good representation of playground. Dimensions are indicated. Length and width of playground are subdivided for ease of locating dinosaurs. All eight dinosaurs are positioned, with length and width correctly indicated. (Level 3)

▶ Diagram shows correct measurements of playground. Some attempt is made to subdivide the side lengths, but there are some errors. Some dinosaurs are positioned fairly accurately, but others show student is not always thinking about the relationships between the dinosaur's dimensions and the dimensions of the playground. (Level 2)

▶ Diagram may not indicate measurements of playground. Only one or two dinosaurs are placed on the diagram, and there is no relationship between the dimensions of the dinosaurs and the dimensions of the playground. (Level 1)

## About the Interview Assessment Task

As students work during Along The Way, ask individual students, **Why are you making your dinosaur drawing that size? How does it relate to the life-size dimensions?**

## Possible Responses

In real life, this dinosaur is 12 feet high and 25 feet long, so I'm making him 12 inches by 25 inches. This grid will help me draw in the details.

*Understands the scale-drawing process. Shows facility with the ratio 1 inch = 1 foot in making the dinosaur drawing on 1-inch grid paper. (Level 3)*

Each one of these boxes stands for 1 foot in real life. This dinosaur is 26 feet long so I counted out 26 boxes. It's 9 feet tall so I'll count up 9 boxes. Then I'll pick one of these grids that makes the picture 9 boxes tall.

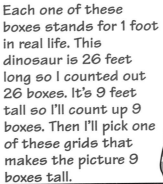

*Has a concrete understanding of the grid paper to life-size relationships. Understands how to select a grid overlay. (Level 3)*

I made my grid paper the right size—see, 12 feet by 23 feet. But I don't know what to do with these grids.

*Understands the 1 inch = 1 foot relationship, but is confused by the use of the transparent grid overlays. (Level 2)*

I cut out this grid paper by counting squares for feet. Now I'm going to look at this picture and sketch in the dinosaur.

*Correctly creates a to-scale sketch, but does not incorporate the cell-to-cell drawing technique. (Level 2)*

## Portfolio Review

At the end of this week review each student's work using the guidelines below. Record your findings on a copy of the Performance Observations recording sheet on page 110.

**In the Portfolio:**
- Scale Drawings of dinosaurs
- Writing about drawing to scale

What to look for
in the students' work:

- Is the student able to create to-scale drawings using grid paper and dinosaur pictures?

- Does the student's report indicate an understanding of scale drawing and steps for making one?

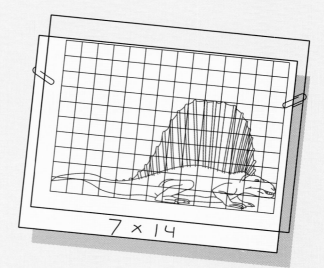

7 x 14

## What You Might See

▶ Has several scale drawings of different dinosaurs and all show accurate dimensions. Writing includes terminology and descriptions that indicate confidence with the idea and process of making scale drawings. (Level 3)

▶ Has at least one scale drawing with accurate dimensions. Writing shows some understanding of the scale-drawing concept, but there are some confused ideas. (Level 2)

▶ Has drawings that are not to-scale or has no completed drawings. Writing does not show an understanding of the scale-drawing concept, and understanding is not evident even in an oral discussion. (Level 1)

**Week 4**
**Amazing Relationships**
Interview Assessment

## About the Interview Assessment

As students work during Along the Way, ask individual students, *Which object are you writing a clue for now? Tell me about your thinking as you make up your clue.*

## Possible Responses

We're working on the Ferris wheel. I'll look for a dinosaur that's either not as tall or taller. Then I'll figure out a clue for that. A Maiasaura is 15 feet tall. That's half as tall as the Ferris wheel. Now I have to put in a clue about the width.

*Clearly understands the clue-writing process and finds sophisticated relationships between the object and the dinosaur. (Level 3)*

I'm doing a bookshelf. The clue is "Its height is 3 feet shorter than Triceratops and its width is 6 feet less than Triceratops' height."

*Understands the clue-writing process, and finds accurate relationships between dinosaurs and objects. (Level 3)*

Well, we're doing a bike right now. My clue says, "It's ten feet shorter than a Tyrannosaurus."

*Understands the clue-writing process, but suggests a clue involving an incorrect comparison or does not specify length or width. (Level 2)*

I'm writing a clue about a ladder. I'll say that it's tall and skinny and you can climb it.

*Does not understand the object of the clue-writing activity. Needs further teacher guidance. (Level 1)*

## Portfolio Review

At the end of this week review each student's work using the guidelines below. Record your findings on a copy of the Performance Observations recording sheet on page 110.

### What to look for in the students' work:

- Is the student able to solve a Comparison Clues puzzle using dinosaur data and estimation skills?

- Is the student able to create a Comparison Clues puzzle, writing statements with correct mathematical relationships?

- Is the student able to describe several Amazing Relationships, correlating dinosaur data and real-world information?

### In the Portfolio:
- Comparison Clue solutions
- Explanation recording
- Puzzle and Answer recording
- Object and Dimension list
- Amazing Relationships recording

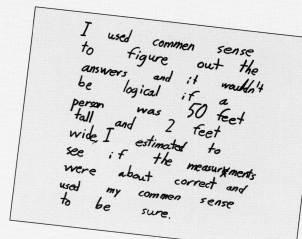

## What You Might See

▶ Correctly solves the original Comparison Clues puzzle and other puzzles made by classmates. Creates a Comparison Clues puzzle that can be solved by classmates. Describes several Amazing Relationships, accurately comparing information. (Level 3)

▶ Solves Comparison Clues puzzles created by others, but has difficulty writing the statements necessary to create one. Reports at least one interesting and correct Amazing Relationship. (Level 2)

▶ Has difficulty interpreting the information necessary to create or solve a Comparison Clues puzzle even when it is read aloud. Also has difficulty making comparison statements telling an Amazing Relationship. (Level 1)

# Week 5
# Supersaurus Stumpers
## Interview Assessment

## About the Interview Assessment

As the class works during Along the Way, ask individual students, *What problem are you working on now? Tell me about your strategies for solving it.*

## Possible Responses

How many strides would it take me to go half a mile? A mile is 2640 feet. My stride is 3 feet, so how many threes are there in 2640? I'll divide on my calculator. 880 steps in a mile, 440 steps in half a mile!

*Uses a logical solution process. Uses a calculator to solve the problem successfully. (Level 3)*

We're figuring how long it takes Supersaurus to walk a mile. It takes 12 minutes to go half a mile. That makes 24 minutes for a mile.

*Uses a logical solution process. Uses mental math strategies to solve the problem. (Level 3)*

How many of me would it take to weigh the same as Supersaurus? I weigh 70 pounds, and Supersaurus weighs 75 tons! Maybe 100 of me? No, that's 700 pounds. What's a ton? 2000 pounds. How many 70s in 2000?

*Uses some logical techniques for solving the problem, but gets confused midway. (Level 2)*

I wanted to see how far a fourth-grader could walk in an hour, but I just can't tell.

*Is unable to start the problem, even with some hints from teacher. (Level 1)*

## Portfolio Review

At the end of this week review each student's work using the guidelines below. Record your findings on a copy of the Performance Observations recording sheet on page 110.

### What to look for in the students' work:

- Is the student able to make a recording showing the solutions for several Supersaurus Stumpers?

- Does the student's work include words or drawings to explain the solution and the methods used?

- Is the student's recording organized in a way that makes the solutions and findings easy to follow?

**In the Portfolio:**
- Supersaurus Stumper recording
- Mile-Long Parade recording

Height: 5½ ft.
Weight: 85 pounds
Stride length: 2ft.
Number of strides: 111 ft.

Height: 58"
Weight: 77 lbs.    4'10" About 5'
Stride: 23"  About 2'
No. of strides per 100 yards: 138.

## What You Might See

▶ Recordings show an organized approach to the solution of several related groups of Supersaurus problems. The presentation of the solutions includes not only the answer, but information about the student's thinking. (Level 3)

▶ Has solutions for several problems in the recordings. A few problem solutions include diagrams or descriptions of method, but others are missing this information. (Level 2)

▶ Recordings are sketchy and difficult to interpret even when the student is interviewed. (Level 1)

# Unit 9
# Dinosaur Days
## Written Assessment

## About the Written Assessment Task

This assessment gives you an opportunnity to see students' written responses to a particular question related to the unit. It is not an evaluation of the entire unit. Use this task anytime during the unit or as a pre-unit assessment. You may also use this task with just a few students when you need extra insight into their mathematical thinking.

Since this unit asks students to apply a variety of mathematical skills and concepts in a real-life setting, this assessment task focuses on the students' awareness of the uses of mathematics in the world around them.

**Materials:** Each student will need a full sheet of paper.

**Assessment Task:** Tell the students, *Think of some ways in which math is used by people every day. Use words, pictures, and numbers to tell about your ideas. Tell at least three ways.*

## Possible Responses

Math is used every day by people to counting bills, for games, playing music, and cooking. Counting bill as in 2 bill each for 105 dollers equals 210 to pay to "so and so". Games as in math games like 5×5- 2+95÷68=1.735. Playing music as in 6 beats per measer and the 8th note gets the beat = 8 time. Cooking as in 2 cups of flour and 1½ cups of oil.

◄ Student shows many ways in which math is used and presents this using a combination of words, pictures, and numbers. (Level 3)

◀ Student shows one way math is used every day and presents this in a clear and understandable manner. Might be able to tell more ways given time. (Level 2)

Student draws some pictures, and tells how they are related to math. (Level 2) ▶

# UNIT 10

## Unit 10
## 'Round They Go
### Assessment Overview

### Before the Unit

Several types of assessment are available as you work with your class during this unit:

- Classroom Observations
- Interview Assessments (pages 104, 106)
- Math Journal (Guidebook, page 341)
- Written Assessment (pages 108–109)
- Self-Assessment (Guidebook, page 350)
- Portfolio Reviews (pages 105, 107)

The goal is for students to move toward an understanding of the Key Mathematical Ideas and to focus on the Communication Characteristics and Learning Dispositions listed below. Observations, interviews, portfolio materials, and students' self-assessments should all contribute to your overall impression of each student's understanding. It is important to use multiple sources of information to obtain valid inferences of each student's learning over time.

## Use these guidelines as you observe students' work throughout the unit:

| Key Mathematical Ideas | Communication Characteristics | Learning Dispositions |
|---|---|---|
| ★ The greater the probability of an event, the more often the event can be expected to occur. <br><br> ★ The greater the number of trials of an experiment, the closer the experimental probability will be to the mathematical probability. <br><br> ★ The probability of a particular event can be expressed in fractional notation. | ★ Did the student make clear and organized recordings? <br><br> ★ Did the student show originality in designing a carnival game? | ★ Was the student enthusiastic and curious about performing experiments? <br><br> ★ Did the student's recordings show attention to detail? <br><br> ★ Did the student show responsibility in carefully designing and playing carnival games? |

You can use this generalized rubric as a suggested guide as you look at students' work and listen to their responses. You may wish to adapt this rubric to make it more task-specific. Share your rubric with your class so that they can take responsibility for monitoring their own learning. ▶

**Response Levels**

3 Accomplishes the purposes of the question, task, or unit. Mathematical communication is clear.

2 Partially accomplishes the purposes of the question, task, or unit. Mathematical communication is somewhat limited.

1 Shows fragmented understanding. Mathematical communication is vague.

## After the Unit

Once the class has completed work on this unit, pull together the various pieces listed below and make an overall evaluation of each student's performance. Record your summary on a copy of the Unit Evaluation recording sheet on page 111. You can use the completed Unit Evaluation sheet and the student's portfolio to give family members a picture of their child's progress.

 **Written Assessment**

'Round They Go Written Assessment, pages 108–109

 **Interview Assessment**

Week 1 • Spinning Wheels Interview
page 104

Week 2 • Carnival Games Interview
page 106

 **Portfolio Review**

Week 1    • Two Spinners and descriptions
page 105  • Experiments 1 to 4 recordings
          • Spinner Game recordings

Week 2    • Carnival Game
page 107  • Day at the Carnival recording

Note: In addition to the Portfolio Review work listed here, Home Work and Side Trip work may also have been included in the students' portfolios. See In the Portfolio, Guidebook, page 350.

 **Observation**    **Math Journal**    **Self-Assessment**

Use any notes you made while observing students work, the students' Math Journal entries, and their written Self-Assessment pieces as further insights into their mathematical thinking.

## UNIT 10

### Week 1
### Spinning Wheels
### Interview Assessment

## About the Interview Assessment Task

As pairs work during Along the Way, show two spinners and a tally sheet to individual students. Ask, *With which spinner do you think you would be more likely to get this tally sheet?*

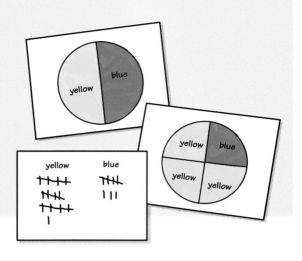

## Possible Responses

Spinner 2, because it's $\frac{3}{4}$ yellow, and Spinner 1 is only $\frac{1}{2}$ yellow.

*Chooses the spinner with more yellow, giving as a reason the relative sizes of sample space. Uses language of fractions to explain. (Level 3)*

Spinner 2, because there is a lot more yellow space so the spinner would land on yellow more.

*Chooses the spinner with more yellow, giving as a reason the relative sizes of sample space. (Level 3)*

It could be either spinner because they both have blue and yellow.

*Determines that it could be either spinner because both spinners could spin blue or yellow. Does not commit as to which is more likely. (Level 2)*

Either spinner, because it seems like I always spin yellow.

*Chooses spinner without regard to sample space, according to ideas of luck or other irrelevant ideas. (Level 1)*

## Portfolio Review

 At the end of this week review each student's work using the guidelines below. Record your findings on a copy of the Performance Observations recording sheet on page 110.

### What to look for in the students' work:

- Is the student able to make two spinners, one that gave even and one that gave uneven chances of winning?

- Is the student able to use fraction language to talk about the probability of spinning a certain color?

- Is the student able to make thoughtful predictions about spinner experiments and test and record the results of the experiments?

**In the Portfolio:**
- Two Spinners and descriptions
- Experiments 1 to 4 recordings
- Spinner Game recording

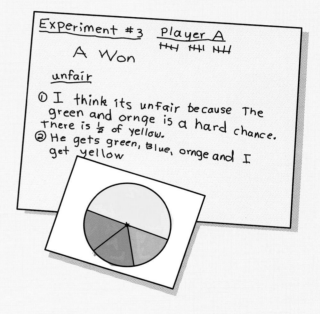

## What You Might See

▶ Makes spinners that give even and uneven chances of winning. Is able to talk about the spinners using fraction language to describe the sample space. Writings about probability experiments indicate that student based predictions on sample space. (Level 3)

▶ Makes spinners that give even and uneven chances of winning. Is able to use fraction language to talk about the possibilities of some of the spinners. In writing about spinner experiments, student is hesitant to commit to predictions. (Level 2)

▶ Makes several spinners, but is unable to discuss them in terms of fairness or fractions. Records results of spins, but writing does not indicate attempt to analyze probabilities. (Level 1)

# UNIT 10

## Week 2
## Carnival Games
### Interview Assessment

## About the Interview Assessment Task

As students are working this week, show individual students two spinners and ask, *Which spinner would be more likely to spin blue? Why do you think so?*

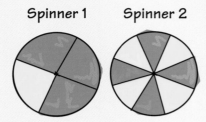

Spinner 1    Spinner 2

## Possible Responses

Spinner 1, because it is $\frac{3}{4}$ blue, and the other spinner only has, let's see, $\frac{4}{8}$ blue.

*Indicates the spinner with more blue and accurately uses fraction language to explain the relative probability. (Level 3)*

Spinner 1, because it has more blue space.

*Indicates spinner with more blue, giving as a reason the amount of blue in sample space. (Level 3)*

They both have blue, so you could spin blue on either one.

*May be aware of difference in sample space, but is not willing to commit to one choice as more likely than the other. (Level 2)*

I could spin blue on either spinner. Blue is my favorite color and I spin it really often.

*Answer is based on idea of luck rather than sample space. (Level 1)*

## Response Levels

**3** Accomplishes the purposes of the question, task, or unit. Mathematical communication is clear.

**2** Partially accomplishes the purposes of the question, task, or unit. Mathematical communication is somewhat limited.

**1** Shows fragmented understanding. Mathematical communication is vague.

## Portfolio Review

At the end of this week review each student's work using the guidelines below. Record your findings on a copy of the Performance Observations recording sheet on page 110.

### What to look for in the students' work:

- Is the student able to work cooperatively with the group to create an interesting carnival game with one or more spinners?

- When choosing carnival games to play, does the student demonstrate understanding of the probability of winning with specific spinners?

**In the Portfolio:**
- Carnival Game
- Day at the Carnival recording

## What You Might See

▶ Works cooperatively with group members to create a carnival game. Demonstrates understanding of probability both in creating and in playing carnival games. (Level 3)

▶ Works cooperatively with group members to create a carnival game. When playing games, demonstrates some understanding of the probability of winning with certain spinners but does not analyze them closely. (Level 2)

▶ Has difficulty working cooperatively with group members. When playing games, demonstrates little understanding of the influence of probability, but relies on the luck of the spin. (Level 1)

# Unit 10
# 'Round They Go
Written Assessment

## About the Written Assessment Task

This assessment gives you an opportunity to see students' written responses to a particular question related to the unit. It is not an evaluation of the entire unit. Use this task anytime duing the unit or as a pre-unit assessment. You may also use this task with just a few students when you need extra insight into their mathematical thinking.

This assessment task focuses on students' understanding of the probability of certain chance events' occurring and their ability to communicate probabilities in writing.

**Materials:** Each student will need a full sheet of paper, a pencil and crayons.

**Assessment Task:** Show a spinner that is divided into sixths. Every other sixth is yellow; one sixth is green; and two sixths are blue. Ask, *What are the chances of spinning blue? Write what you think. Tell why you think so.*

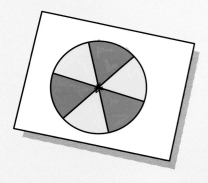

## Possible Responses

I think it will land on blue 2 times out of six. or $\frac{2}{6}$ or $\frac{1}{3}$ Because half of three sixths are yellow Three yellow minus 1 green equals 2 blue. If you spin 30 times you might land on blue 10 times, yellow 15 times, and green 5 times.

◄ Student's writing says that there is a one-in-three chance, or one third, of spinning blue. (Level 3)

1. I think you have a pretty good chance because there is two blues that is allmost half. You have a better chance of geting blue than green.

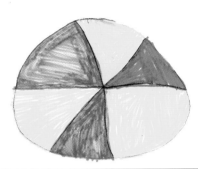

◄ Student estimates the chance. Understands that there is a better chance of getting blue than green. (Level 2)

Student thinks chance of getting blue is based on trying to get it. (Level 1) ▶

I think you can because you just have to see its a matter of trying to get blue or not some times you will some times you won't thats how I think you can get blue or you can't.

# Performance Observations

**Unit** _____

**Assessment Task** _____

_____

| Student | Date | Level | Observations |
|---------|------|-------|--------------|
|  |  |  |  |
|  |  |  |  |
|  |  |  |  |
|  |  |  |  |
|  |  |  |  |
|  |  |  |  |
|  |  |  |  |
|  |  |  |  |
|  |  |  |  |
|  |  |  |  |
|  |  |  |  |
|  |  |  |  |
|  |  |  |  |
|  |  |  |  |
|  |  |  |  |
|  |  |  |  |
|  |  |  |  |
|  |  |  |  |
|  |  |  |  |
|  |  |  |  |
|  |  |  |  |

## Unit Evaluation

Date _____

Unit _____

Student _____

| Assessment Task | Date | Level | Observations |
|---|---|---|---|
| | | | |
| | | | |
| | | | |
| | | | |
| | | | |
| | | | |
| | | | |
| | | | |
| | | | |
| | | | |
| | | | |
| | | | |
| | | | |

**Summary Comments**

Unit Evaluation
To the Teacher: Permission is given to reproduce this page.

MathLand™ Grade 4 • Assessment Guide
© Creative Publications
**111**

# BIBLIOGRAPHY

Association for Supervision and Curriculum Development, Evito Perrone, (ed.). *Expanding Student Assessment.* Alexandria, VA: The Association. 1991.

Charles, Randall, Frank Lester, and Phares O'Daffer. *How to Evaluate Progress in Problem Solving.* Reston, VA: National Council of Teachers of Mathematics. 1987.

Charles, Randall and Edward Silver. *Research Agenda for Mathematics Education: The Teaching and Assessing of Mathematical Problem Solving, Vol 3.* Reston, VA: National Council of Teachers of Mathematics. 1989.

Clarke, David. *The Mathematics Curriculum and Teaching Program: Professional Development Package Assessment Alternatives in Mathematics.* Moorooka, Queensland, Australia: Curriculum Development Centre of Canberra. 1988.

Educational Testing Service. *Mathematics Objectives 1990 Assessment.* Princeton, NJ: Educational Testing Service. 1988.

EQUALS Staff and the Assessment Committee of the California Mathematics Council. *Assessment Alternatives in Mathematics: An Overview of Assessment Techniques that Promote Learning.* Berkeley, CA: Lawrence Hall of Science, University of California. 1989.

Herman, Joan L., Pamela R. Aschbacher, and Lynn Winters. *A Practical Guide to Alternative Assessment.* Alexandria, VA: Association for Supervision and Curriculum Development. 1992.

Kamii, Constance. *Achievement Testing in the Early Grades: The Games Grown-Ups Play.* Washington, DC: National Association for the Education of Young Children. 1990.

Lambdin, Diana V., et al. *Emphasis on Assessment: Readings from NCTM's School-Based Journals.* Reston, VA: National Council of Teachers of Mathematics. 1996.

Leinwand, Steven. *Connecticut's Mathematics Performance Assessment Project.* Hartford, CT: Connecticut Department of Education. 1990.

Massachusetts Department of Education. *On Their Own: Student Response to Open-Ended Tests in Mathematics.* Quincy, MA: The Department. 1989.

Moon, Jean and Linda Schulman. *Finding the Connections: Linking Assessment, Instruction, and Curriculum in Elementary Mathematics.* Portsmouth, NH: Heinemann. 1995.

NCTM Commission on Standards for School Mathematics. *Assessment Standards for School Mathematics.* Reston, VA: The Council. 1993.

NCTM Commission on Standards for School Mathematics. *Curriculum and Evaluation Standards for School Mathematics.* Reston, VA: The Council. 1989.

NCTM Commission on Standards for School Mathematics. *Professional Standards for Teaching Mathematics.* Reston, VA: The Council. 1989.

Paulson, Leon. *Portfolio Guides in Primary Math.* Portland, OR: Multnomah Education Service District. 1994.

Richardson, Kathy. *A Look at Children's Thinking.* Norman, OK: Educational Enrichment. 1990.

Stenmark, Jean Kerr, ed. *Mathematics Assessment: Myths, Models, Good Questions, and Practical Suggestions.* Reston, VA: National Council of Teachers of Mathematics. 1991.

Webb, N. L., and A. F. Coxford, eds. *Assessment in the Mathematics Classroom.* Reston, VA: National Council of Teachers of Mathematics. 1993.

Note: Your state's mathematics framework is another good guide to assessment practices.